Openings

Alan & Celia Younger

Hodder & Stoughton

A MEMBER OF THE HODDER HEADLINE GROUP

British Library Cataloguing in Publication Data
Younger, Alan
Openings
1. Moral education (Elementary)
I. Title II. Younger, Celia
372.8

ISBN 0 340 670 231

First published 1997
Impression number 10 9 8 7 6 5 4 3 2 1
Year 1999 1998 1997

Typeset by Fakenham Photosetting Limited
Printed in Great Britain for Hodder & Stoughton Educational, a division of Hodder Headline Plc, 338 Euston Road, London NW1 3BH by Athenaeum Press, Newcastle-upon-Tyne.

Contents

Acknowledgements

This book is dedicated to the memory of Rosemary Knight. Thank you for your encouragement and your friendship, which meant so much to us.

Alan and Celia

The authors would like to thank the following individuals and organisations for all their help, advice and support:

Rosaline Nesbitt	The Family and Child Health Department Dumfries and Galloway
ChildLine	Studd Street London N1 0QW
The Anti-bullying Campaign	10 Borough High Street London SE1 9QQ
Kidscape	152 Buckingham Palace Road, London SW1W 9TR
Dumfries And Galloway Constabulary	Cornwall Mount Dumfries
Carers National Association	20–25 Glasshouse Yard, London EC1A 4JS
National Asthma Campaign	Providence House Providence Place London N1 0NT
Gwen Kirkwood	

Introduction

How this book can be useful to you

These short stories are designed to give teachers, and those who work with children, an opportunity – an 'opening' – to discuss important social, moral and health concerns. Although it was created specifically with classroom situations in mind, this book can also be of value to anyone whose aim is to support young children and their families. Used in a sensitive way, these stories will allow children to discuss their own worries or problems by transposing them onto the fictitious characters in Bradwell School. Children will find this less threatening than being questioned or directly confronted.

The stories can be used in any order since each of the stories is complete and can be read aloud at one session of about ten to fifteen minutes. It is not intended that this book should be read as a novel, but that the stories should be selected and used when needed.

The stories are all set in the fictitious town of Bradwell, and children will quickly become familiar with the central characters of Bradwell School. It is similar to many ordinary neighbourhood Primary or Junior schools. The children in the class which forms the main focus of the book are in the 6–10 year age range, although older children may still empathise with many of the characters, depending on their own level of maturity. The specific age of the children in the stories is not revealed. There is one class teacher, Miss Forman, who is involved in the usual interaction between herself and other members of the staff, children and parents. The children in her class present problems that many class-teachers will recognise. Sometimes these issues are best dealt with in a 1:1 situation with the child concerned, but frequently there are issues which benefit from being discussed by the whole class or a group, in such a way that none of the class feel threatened and that the individuals can maintain anonymity.

The key issues arising from each story are identified to enable teachers to select the appropriate one quickly. An outline of the main theme of each story is given in the section entitled 'Key Issues'. There are also suggestions, simple guidelines and some useful addresses which are of particular relevance to each story. Children will probably suggest conclusions and outcomes, sometimes without being prompted, but they will need guidance backed by relevant factual information in order to make well-informed opinions about the issues raised in the stories. Home circumstances, parental attitudes and influences such as friends or the media will affect their judgment. It is necessary to value each contribution while at the same time gently guide their thinking so that they recognise outlandish and irrational viewpoints. It is crucial that teachers do not dismiss unusual ideas, and it is also important that one's own value judgments are not imposed upon children. They will find it more meaningful to develop their own values through supportive discussion. This is not an easy process for every child but it is important to try to develop their understanding and awareness of themselves and society by encouraging thinking and questioning.

It is not always necessary for children to arrive at a conclusion or create a suitable ending for each story, and sometimes it is inappropriate to expect one. The success of the story as a teaching aid relies on the depth and meaningfulness of the discussion more than finding satisfactory conclusions.

Occasionally, older pupils may find these stories to be a good stimulus for imaginative writing, but they were not created primarily as a prompt for written work. Discussion, the exchange of ideas and the questioning of each other's values will be far more productive than writing. However, writing could be an acceptable medium through which a particularly shy child might express ideas.

All of the characters in this book are fictitious.

Key Issues

In order to make it easy and quick to select the most appropriate story to suit individual needs, there follows a brief outline of each of the stories. Included are some guidelines giving examples of suggested outcomes, approaches and references which may be useful.

Simon's Story

'Simon's Story' explores a spontaneous and unpremeditated classroom theft and views this behaviour from a child's perspective. It exposes clues to the probable underlying causes of the theft, although some immature children may find this a little difficult to understand at first. The concept that unhappiness can lead to irrational behaviour can be explored further with the teacher. Classroom thefts are sometimes the result of a joke that went wrong or a thoughtless action in an idle moment with no deep-rooted cause, so the story leaves this as another possibility. However, Simon is old enough to recognise that adults take stealing very seriously and he is aware of what he has done even if he is unable to analyse why. He relies on his friend to support his decision to own up.

This story gives the teacher an opportunity to investigate suitable endings which may reflect an individual or a school's policy on discipline. There are various options for the children to consider. They might suggest that Simon's courage and honesty are rewarded by a more lenient punishment. Alternatively, it might be decided that his own conscience has punished him sufficiently overnight. Simon may be in a position to monitor his own behaviour and give suggestions for his own punishment, or it may be suggested that the school's policy on discipline is not negotiable. The children may consider ways in which Simon receives support to prevent a similar incident occurring. Children are likely to offer a wide variety of sanctions and solutions.

Simon and Joe's relationship is also an element of the story that could lead to discussion about the qualities of friendships, and strategies to help Simon's shyness could be investigated.

Bully For You

Bullying is a common word used to describe dominating unwanted behaviour imposed by one person onto another. Children tend to believe that bullying is always physical and violent and are often unaware of the more subtle forms such as verbal abuse, ridicule and systematic isolation. Verbal bullying can be as devastating as physical bullying to the victim despite there being no apparent physical signs of abuse. However, even verbal assaults can be differentiated by their subtlety. A bully may use blatant or repeated verbal attacks, or alternatively can slowly or systematically erode a victim's confidence and self-esteem. These methods of bullying are more discrete and can often be hidden behind a 'cloak of friendship' making the victim unsure of how to interpret what is happening. This uncertainty on the part of the victim can be further enhanced when a dominating child learns how to manipulate others in the group so that they carry out the actual bullying.

In 'Bully For You', Graham is confused by conflicting signals from Rory who appears to be a friend, yet produces sudden physical attacks as he smiles and laughs. Graham is very friendly towards the owner of a pet shop, and she witnesses one of Rory's intimidating attacks. She persuades Graham to confide in her, and together they discuss ways of stopping Rory's bullying.

Children can be encouraged to consider different forms of bullying which may help them to quickly identify less overt tactics such as isolation, verbal attacks, and manipulation of either the victim or members of the peer group. It may be that the bully is physically strong, but other characteristics can empower a bully, such as being quick with words, or sharp-witted. No matter which approach is adopted, bullying is perpetuated where it is shrouded in secrecy.

Children need guidance to differentiate between brief short-lived disagreements and systematic, sustained bullying. There will also need to be a clear outline of the school's or establishment's policy and the sanctions that will be taken against the bully. It will be reassuring for them to understand that exposing a bully would not be considered as tale-telling and that it definitely could *not* make the situation worse.

The following organisations make a selection of materials available to adults who have a concern about the welfare of children, and they advocate giving the children direct access to the phone numbers and addresses of their organisations.

ChildLine – a free national helpline providing a confidential phone counselling service to listen, comfort and protect.

Administration address: ChildLine
2nd Floor Royal Mail Buildings
Studd Street
London N1 0QW
Address for Children: ChildLine
Freepost 1111
London N1 0BR
Telephone Helpline: 0800 1111 (24 hours per day)
ChildLine for children in care: 0800 884444 (6 p.m. to 10 p.m. daily)
Hearing Impaired Helpline – Minicom 0800 400222 (2 p.m. to 9 p.m. daily)

The Anti-Bullying Campaign (please send a large stamped addressed envelope)
10, Borough High Street
London SE1 9QQ
Telephone 0171 378 1446

Kidscape (please send a large stamped addressed envelope)
152, Buckingham Palace Road
London SW1W 9TR
Telephone 0171 730 3300

A Video Nasty

Lynzi and her sister Katie are encouraged to watch videos that have been brought into their home by the baby-sitter because this keeps the sisters entertained while she completes her homework. Lynzi enjoys the horror videos and is only mildly affected by them, whereas Katie is more sensitive and is easily scared. Although Katie is curious and is drawn to watch them when other people are in the room, she always becomes very frightened at night when it is dark or she is on her own. Sometimes she wets the bed when she is too frightened to go to the toilet, and she hides her damp nighties in her chest of drawers because she is too embarrassed to tell her mother.

This story does not centre on the content of the video itself, but on Katie's emotions when she goes to bed, her fear of the dark and her inability to sleep. When she needs to go to the toilet at about 3 o' clock in the morning, her mother discovers her secret and they begin to talk about the effects that the videos are having on Katie.

It would be helpful if children could examine cassettes displaying the symbols for viewing suitability to help them recognise appropriate tapes. These are normally displayed in either a triangle or circle on the video's box and on the cassette itself.

U: means universal – suitable for all ages.
UC: indicates that the film is 'universal' and especially produced for children.
PG: are the initials for 'parental guidance'. Parents are required to decide whether or not this video is suitable for *their* own child.
E: films displaying this symbol are exempt from censorship. Music and sports videos do not have to comply with the same censorship regulations. They may contain violence and nudity which is unsuitable for children.
12 / **15** / **18**: this is the minimum age for viewing or renting, and these videos should not knowingly be sold or rented to anyone under the specified age.

Fortunately, some manufacturers are acting very responsibly by using additional coding systems of their own to indicate the level of violence, strong language, sex and nudity and type of theme or contents. This code system is currently specific to each manufacturer and can be found on the box and the cassette, but is often not easily interpreted by children. They would then require some assistance from an older person, and could be encouraged to ask the sales person at the video rental shop for advice when they are having difficulties.

It is important that any follow-up to this story does not focus on the content of the videos in too much depth, as this will frighten some children. It is likely that some children will want to boast about the videos they have watched, probably suggesting that they were not frightened by them. They could be reminded that both adults and children vary in their use of imagination and their sensitivity to exposure to violence and horror. Teachers may also point out how easily videos can be watched, but how difficult it is to forget scenes, especially when in frightening situations. It could also be explained that when children watch any television, it is very easy to become confused between reality and fiction. This can be demonstrated by asking children if the latest 'soap series' is portraying real life, then what about the 'News'? Discussion can then follow about how viewers recognise reality, yet can be fooled by good acting or a convincing story line.

Daredevils and Chickens

There is a game that children, particularly boys, play during which they jump in front of moving cars with the object of startling the driver and proving to their peers that they have a lot of courage. Children can be coerced into this game because they are intimidated by others. Some children enjoy this game because they believe that a car is capable of stopping within a few seconds and they are ignorant of the pain and damage inflicted by a moving car. Teachers might find it useful to substitute the local name for this game so that their pupils recognise it more easily.

The aim of this story is to highlight the dangers of the game without having to adopt what is often perceived as a preaching or nagging stance, since it focuses on the boys in the story rather than individuals in the classroom.

The story illustrates how the effects of the game are further reaching than children are aware. Peter is the most obvious victim of the game, but Robin and his family, and the van driver are also traumatised by it. The story concentrates on Miss Forman's genuine concern for her pupils rather than any annoyance or irritation she may feel about the disruption of her evening and morning drives.

During follow-up discussions, children might be able to talk about other games which have a similar 'daredevil' element. There may be an opportunity to investigate safe games and dangerous games, which may be particularly relevant if the school is situated near water, railway or major road.

The Cat and the Slippers

Children tend to ask direct questions about death and can often challenge adult beliefs. Sometimes, especially when an adult has no strong convictions about death, there is a fear that these questions will be impossible to answer and that, as a result, the child will be inconsolable. Therefore, adults often look to other sources such as the Bible, the Qur'an or secular stories to provide the answers to the child's questions.

In this story, Miss Forman uses a secular book in the hope that it will help George to cope with the death of his Nana. Her book helps to open the topic for discussion, but not in the way that she had anticipated. The story about the dog angers George, who finds it unacceptable and inappropriate. She tries to explain how some of the suggestions in the story might help him, but at the end of their discussion she feels that he may not have understood, and so she leaves him to draw a picture.

Unknown to her, George takes the picture of Nana's cat home and places it in a box with her old slippers. From now on, whenever he sees his picture of Smokey next to Nana's slippers he knows that it will trigger all the memories of his Nana. From then on he is not afraid that he may forget her.

This story explores only one aspect of bereavement – anxiety that the deceased person may be forgotten, which highlights the need for something tangible to use as a stimulus for the memory. This is a very sensitive subject and so there should be the opportunity for each child to contribute to the discussion, if they wish to. This makes small pupil discussion groups more appropriate here than larger class groupings. Children should be encouraged to focus on the methods people employ so that they do not forget close friends and family who have died. Examples of this include, erecting a headstone, making a collection of photographs and mementos, dedicating a trophy, providing a plaque, planting a tree or favourite shrub, visiting a grave, bequeathing a gift to a hospital or charity, writing a song or poem, setting up a trust fund and writing an 'in memorium' for a local newspaper. They are intended to be symbolic and long-lasting evidence of someone's life. They reassure the bereaved that even if their memories begin to fade there is a physical stimulus to act as a trigger and enhance that memory.

Children may disagree with George's assumption that the death of an animal is not as painful as the death of a person. George also believes that unless a person has experienced bereavement for themselves, they cannot experience the intensity of the pain, or have genuine sympathy for someone who has. This could lead to further valuable discussions with more mature children.

At the Bottom of the Garden

This short story gives an explicit and hard-hitting account of the consequences of a solvent-abusing session that was held in a garden shed by a group of boys. It may have been their first attempt, or it may have been one of their regular meetings, but on this occasion it had an almost tragic ending for Joe. He was abandoned by his friends, perhaps through fear of being discovered themselves, but more probably because they were suffering from the effects of the fumes as well. They were seen staggering through the vegetable patch in Mr Braithwaite's garden and as a result Joe was discovered in a critical condition in the shed.

When children are told that 'glue-sniffing' or other solvent abuse is dangerous and can ultimately cause brain damage or even death, they often have no real understanding of what this means. That is why this story describes in detail the confusion and distress experienced by Joe on his way to hospital and during the first twenty-four hours of his recovery. It highlights the panic and fear caused by impairment of physical movement. It describes Joe's nausea and the stinging of his skin as the glue is removed from his face, and the pain of the damaged membranes lining his nose and mouth.

Throughout the story there is encouragement and reassurance from a nurse whom Joe eventually sees as his vision stabilises.

This story does not glamorise Joe's hospitalisation, nor does it portray him as a hero. By describing his helplessness – even to the extent that he vomits over himself – it gives a clear and poignant picture of one of the possible outcomes of solvent-abuse. It concludes by suggesting that Joe's nightmarish experiences would have been worse if Mr Braithwaite had not acted so responsibly and quickly.

Up to Scratch

An infestation of nits in the classroom leads to a visit by the school nurse to instruct the children about prevention and treatment. Information about lice is reported via the dialogue between the nurse and the pupils in a factual manner, emphasising that lice prefer clean heads and that hair length is relatively unimportant. The story corrects some of the misconceptions about lice and clearly explains the best way to eradicate them, in a light-hearted and amusing way. Children may be able to discuss the attitude of the parents who appear at the end of the story. The first mother clearly has not read the information leaflet that was sent home, nor has she listened to her son. She even refers to the lice as fleas. The second mother appreciates the effort that Miss Forman and the nurse have made to explain the life-history of the louse and the most effective control methods. Pupils may conclude that if Steven's mother does not follow the medical advice, then there will almost certainly be a reinfestation.

Older children may be able to understand why the insecticide lotions need to be rotated on average every three years and controlled centrally by Health Boards to ensure that lice do not become resistant. They may also understand why insecticides should never be used as prophylaxis, (i.e. used as a preventative measure on a person who does not yet have lice) for the same reason.

The control of head-lice is being constantly revised as more is learned about the creatures and traditionally accepted practice is being questioned. For example, there is some debate about the effectiveness of removing the egg-cases of nits with a fine-toothed comb, as some entomologists believe that since the cases are empty or the contents addled, there is little to be gained by removing the cases. Similarly questions are raised about the continued use of shampoos rather than lotions. Each regional authority publishes its own policy, usually distributed via the Health Board. If a school does not have this document it is worth approaching the Regional Health Board as there may be slight regional differences in control methods and advice.

Slippery Snakes

Peter Blenkinsop, known to his friends as Blenco, has been avoiding the police for some time. Each Thursday afternoon he sends his latest shoplifting trainee into a shop while he waits outside. He does not do any of the stealing himself but he coaches younger boys to take the goods and if they are caught he is able to disappear into the crowd. This is the way in which he is 'aiding and abetting' the crime.

Danny is his latest recruit. Several of Danny's predecessors have been caught and like him they were probably too ashamed to tell their school friends about it, and so other boys fall into the same trap.

Danny is caught stealing a mass of sweet jelly snakes, and the game that sounded so exciting suddenly turns into a nightmare. He faces the humiliating experiences of being questioned by the police and the store manager, and being stared at by other customers as he is led back into the shop by a security guard. Worst of all, he is responsible for his mother having to leave her work so that she can be present when he is questioned by the police, and he knows that he has upset and disappointed her. He also has to endure a severe reprimand at the police station the following week.

Blenco runs away as soon as he sees that Danny has been stopped outside the store, and it is clear, by the way he ignores Danny the next day, that his sole interest in Danny was as a shoplifter, working for him.

This story would probably have little impact on a child who has an established history of shoplifting and does not care about the consequences, but it may deter a young child from being persuaded, or dared, by somebody older. It examines some of the things that are liable to happen to a shoplifter once they are caught. It may help children to realise that it is not a game.

Pass it On

A scheme to extort money is already running throughout the classroom and it is only detected when the teacher's intuition is proved to be correct. Clues lead up to the discovery of the scheme – children are suddenly unhappy and there are many secrets. The last clue is revealed when Kevin's parents seek advice about stealing. Secondary pupils are involved because they take money from Ben who, in turn, bullies Kevin and other children. Kevin steals money from home to pay Ben.

Discussion might follow regarding the identity of the victims. There is scope to discuss what might have happened to each of the children had the teacher not intervened. Children may suggest suitable punishments or ways to repair the damage caused by the extortion racket. There are relationships to mend as well as money to repay.

The school's own anti-bullying policy could be discussed and the ChildLine, Anti-Bullying Campaign and Kidscape materials explained. This will reassure children that there are a variety of courses of action for children who feel trapped by this type of bullying.

Although it is implied that money is the currency changing hands, it should be explained that food, sweets, favours, homework etc. are all forms of currency amongst children. As well as supporting victims of extortion, this story might act as a deterrent for any child who thinks of their classmates as easy targets, as it lets them know that there are already strategies in place to identify them.

ChildLine, Anti-Bullying Campaign and Kidscape addresses are given on page iv.

I Can't Breathe

Philip is asthmatic and his attacks are triggered by either exercise or extremely cold air entering his lungs. When he gets into difficulties during PE his friend, Jamail, watches the way that Miss Forman alleviates the asthma attack by staying calm, encouraging him to use his inhaler correctly and offering reassurance.

An unexpected snowstorm closes the school early, and Jamail's mother offers to see Philip home safely, but on the way home he has another attack which is brought about by the severely cold weather conditions. There is no other help available, but Jamail is able to help Philip because he remembers Miss Forman's approach.

This story attempts to give some information about ways in which an asthma sufferer could be helped in an emergency. The asthma attacks are described in a deliberately 'low-key' manner and are not sensationalised in any way. They should not alarm any asthmatic children. This story could be a starting point for discussion about asthma. It may help children to understand why an asthmatic friend cannot run around the football pitch, go out in the cold, keep pets or enjoy certain foods if that is known to be the trigger for their attacks. Classmates might have seen inhalers but not understood their value or use. Since more children suffer from asthma than ever before, it is important that children should feel comfortable about taking their medication and that others in the class understand and support them. Through discussion about asthma, children should be able to realise the importance of getting assistance quickly, or, as in the story, offering reassurance and, if necessary, finding someone's inhaler for them. It should be pointed out that Jamail did not administer the medication. He only made it available for Philip to use himself. Children may need to be reminded that they should never administer medication, or play with inhalers.

Local or Regional support groups for asthma sufferers often have a video and written material which they are able to lend to schools. Sometimes this material is specifically for teacher's or parent's instruction and sometimes it is intended for children's use.

The National Asthma Campaign produces a comprehensive pack of material which is available to schools or individuals who write to this address:

The National Asthma Campaign
Providence House
Providence Place
London N1 0NT

They also provide an Asthma Helpline which is open to callers Monday to Friday, 9 a.m. to 9 p.m. Nursing staff are able to answer direct questions and give counselling to callers who use this phone number: 0345 01 02 03.

The Risk

Calum has recently started to smoke secretly. He was persuaded by a friend who used the argument that not all smokers die from lung cancer. While this is true, his friend conveniently forgot to mention all the other life-threatening illnesses caused directly by smoking. Calum often visits a residential home for elderly people where his mother works. He has a friend there, Mr Thomson, one of the residents, who recognises the signs that Calum has begun to smoke. He reminisces about the last years with his late wife and briefly touches on the way she died. He is trying to warn Calum.

The story is unresolved, and there is no indication whether or not Calum will continue to smoke. Children could decide what they would choose to do in Calum's place.

This is an indirect message about smoking with very little discussion between Mr Thomson and Calum, but it is still hard-hitting because Mr Thomson talks about fact, not speculation. His warning is simply stated.

A selection of material suitable for anti-smoking projects is frequently sent directly to schools. It is usually made available through Regional Health Boards on request.

Campfire Story

Clemmie feels that she is fortunate to have found a school that she can return to each Spring when her family park their caravans on a site outside Bradwell. From a Gypsy family, Clemmie is aware of the hostility towards her people, but she finds that she is accepted in the school and renews her friendships every year. She desperately wants to learn how to read well but her dream to stay at school almost comes to an end when she is assaulted on the way home on the first day.

The story shows the contrast between Clemmie's cleanliness and her attacker's bad breath – suggesting that his standards of hygiene are not as high as hers. Children may not be aware that it is easy to generalise, for example, by presuming that Gypsies are always unclean or that they are unintelligent. Clemmie's father may not have had what he mistakenly refers to as an 'heducation' but he proves that he is intelligent and has, in fact, an exceptionally good memory.

Children may be aware of some of the alternative names for Gypsies such as Romanies or Romany People and Travelling People, as well as the derogatory terms such as Tinker.

This story aims to reinforce the belief that everyone is entitled to be judged by their deeds and actions, not by their race or nationality.

Nadine's New Baby

The arrival of Nadine's new baby brother has temporarily upset her whole world. The equipment he needs is strewn all over the house, his feeding requirements take precedence over anyone else's, and visitors are monopolising her mother. In addition, Nadine is becoming aware that she is no longer the focus of attention by some of her relatives. At school she is more easily upset than usual and a trivial incident results in a fight and a letter being sent home to her family. Nadine's grandpa is her most supportive ally and he understands her feelings and frustrations.

A new baby can be the cause of emotional conflict for children who may feel that they should love the baby when, in fact, they may be resentful or ambivalent towards it. They may feel jealous of the attention it demands, or disappointed because of the size of the baby and its inability to play with them. The difficulties of adjusting emotionally to a baby brother or sister in the home can become apparent at school. 'Nadine's New Baby' gives an opportunity for children to discuss their feelings about young brothers and sisters.

Happy Anniversary

This story is presented as a series of letters exchanged between two school friends. Shamilla had faced a long series of absence from school while she was recovering from a serious accident. She received tuition at home from a teacher, but her main support was from these letters, photographs and pictures which linked her to the outside world of her friends and counteracted the feelings of isolation. Video and audio tapes were also used, with the class producing its own informational newsletter, to help preserve a strong home–school connection.

Shamilla later created a scrapbook from all her correspondence and this played an important part in helping her through the traumatic year. She used it to help herself organise her thoughts about the accident, and she found therapeutic value in looking through the pages as she tried to come to terms with her situation. On the anniversary of the accident, she reopens the scrapbook, not to look through the newspaper cuttings about herself, but to help her think about the friendship and support she had received.

'Happy Anniversary' contains ideas that pupils might consider if one of their classmates is going to be absent for a lengthy period due to illness. It also encourages children to empathise with someone suffering from isolation due to long-term absence from school.

Who Cares?

This is a slightly longer story which explores the effects of a serious illness within the immediate family circle. The pressure that this situation imposes upon a child is made apparent through Elizabeth's inability to cope with the workload at home as well as school. She is exhausted by the daily routine of washing, cleaning, cooking and keeping the house warm, as well as helping Samuel with his reading. She is extremely worried about her mother.

Children might be able to identify Elizabeth's strategies for coping with her extra responsibilities. This story may help them develop empathy with any child who has to act as mother or father for younger siblings and to recognise the need for discipline and cooperation within the family.

There could be several reasons for Elizabeth's mother's illness. Alcoholism, drug-dependency, depression and terminal illness could all be substituted. There are many applications for this story in the classroom. Pupils may be able to suggest ideas that will help Elizabeth even more than those proposed by her school. Among the possibilities are: a rota system for household chores which Samuel could share and make him aware of his responsibility to help keep the house tidy; respite-care; social work intervention; family centre; the Crossroads Organisation, (voluntary sitting service) and other local voluntary groups.

It is now recognised that many hundreds of children are finding themselves in the position of being a carer for a parent, and the organisation that helps adult carers, The Carers National Association, aims to help these children by offering them direct access to support if they contact the address below.

Young Carers
Carers National Association
20–25, Glasshouse Yard
London EC1A 4JS
Telephone 0171 490 8818
A telephone helpline is available between 1 p.m. and 4 p.m. Monday to Friday.

Carers' line 0171 490 8898

I Want to be Like You

This is a story about two friends who buy the same style of fashionable skirt after seeing it in a magazine, but neither of them feel comfortable wearing it. Jodie considers herself to be too overweight, while Sarita feels her legs are too thin. Without realising it, both girls have decided to wear the skirt to the school disco. However, Jodie is so insecure that she is forced to spend the evening in the girls' lavatories, and Sarita misses a lot of the fun because she is looking for Jodie. Both girls have an inaccurate perception of their size and shape. Like so many young people, boys as well as girls, Jodie has been influenced by the media's promotion of 'beauty' without realising that it is artificial. Many children are unaware that most of the vital statistics of top models are outside the average range of height/weight ratios, and that many photographs have been pared down with scissors, enhanced by computer graphics or photographed through special effect filters.

Although magazines frequently feature articles about the dangers of slimming, or promote tolerance of overweight individuals, the advertising still depicts stereotyped model figures.

Many children are influenced so much by advertising and film star images that they become increasingly dissatisfied with their own body shape, regarding themselves as flawed or imperfect. When poor self-image combines with other emotional problems, children can develop illnesses such as anorexia and bulimia nervosa. Very young children can develop these conditions, and there is evidence that poor self-image and a lack of confidence is being reinforced from an early age.

Jodie is avoiding eating regular meals and finds it quite easy to convince people that she is eating normally. Pupils could discuss the need for healthy eating and learn to identify foods most likely to conceal hidden sugars and fats. They could also be advised about deficiency diseases and the effects of severe dieting disorders. They could consider the persuasiveness of advertising and older children may be able to explore how they would choose flattering clothes within current fashion trends. Photographs and video recordings may help children develop confidence and a truer perception of their own appearance, and also illustrate the fact that what they see through their own eyes can be very different to the image that other people see.

Mad Bob

Bob lives in a house on his own. He is given the nick-name of 'Mad Bob' by children who do not understand that his partial deafness and poor eyesight are the reasons for his cautious way of walking and unusual way of speaking. These disabilities force him to move slowly and prevent him from communicating successfully. Bob is vulnerable and becomes easy prey for Dougie, who terrorises him at weekends by yelling abuse and smashing his windows. Mickey is much younger than Dougie and has been drawn into these weekend attacks which he feels are starting to get out of control. He is Dougie's audience and is therefore expected to be impressed. Although he feels that it is wrong to continue breaking the windows he is too afraid to challenge Dougie.

Bob hides in an alleyway with his torch to catch his persecutors. Mickey is coerced into the stone-throwing ritual and Bob grabs him and takes him into the house. Mickey is frightened but soon finds out that Bob has to lip-read and, looking round the house, he realises that Bob has few comforts or possessions. He starts to understand how Bob is isolated by his communication difficulties and the prejudices of other people. He begins to like and respect Bob and there is the suggestion that he might make a return visit as a friend.

Children often adopt the prejudices of others without questioning these values for themselves. This story raises awareness of differences between people. It is Bob's disability which makes him different, but there are many other differences which give rise to prejudice. There may also be an opportunity to open a discussion about the strength of peer pressure, what it is that empowers people, and how that kind of power can be resisted. At the end of the story Mickey faces a dilemma and children may have suggestions about what they feel should happen next.

Going Home

Thomas and his mother have had to move into temporary council accommodation after a big domestic argument. The two of them have a limited amount of money and possessions and are living in a single room at the top of the hostel with some very unpleasant neighbours who party most nights. Thomas is, therefore, tired, angry and insecure and his behaviour ranges from aggressive to withdrawn. He is ashamed of his circumstances, thinking that he is somehow to blame, and he begins to tell lies to cover up. This story demonstrates that a teacher is able to help once all the facts are known, and the relief that a child might feel knowing that there is someone understanding to talk to. This story also gives pupils an insight into what may suddenly change a person's attitude and behaviour and they may be able to identify similar emotional changes in themselves when under stress.

Children will be able to consider what support they would offer to a friend in Thomas' position. This might be in the form of material help, such as books and toys, or they may suggest emotional support in various forms. Debate may develop around the issue of trying to support someone who is acting in an introverted or aggressive manner, and also the way in which external influences affect behaviour patterns and emotions.

Quick! Quick!

Even before she had met them, Mhari forms an opinion about the family that are moving into the 'Big House'. She makes a lot of assumptions about their personalities, mostly based on the evidence of their wealth. She has watched the house renovations and presumes that people who can afford central heating, decorators and double glazing must be mean to their children, and unkind to their pets. She also assumes there will be servants. There is also a hint that she is jealous of the wealthy neighbours she has never seen.

The Big House is a strong contrast to her own shoreside cottage that needs repairing. Mhari's father has to work away from home as a driver, but he has just been laid off because of lack of orders for his employer. Mhari takes for granted her very caring close-knit family.

Mhari's dog runs across quicksand when chasing a wounded seagull and there is danger, first of all for Mhari and her brother Sean who follow, and then for the dog who has to find a safe way back. A man and his daughter are able to help. The girl is quiet and shy and tentatively begins a friendship with Mhari. Later it is discovered that the girl and her father are the new neighbours.

Pupils can discuss the ways in which people can be judged and misjudged, for example, by wealth, accent, race, culture, and even by less obvious criteria such as the sports teams they support and the music they prefer. They may be able to identify how easy it is to generalise, for example, that all Scotsmen are mean and that all Irishmen are not intelligent, etc. Teachers may want to highlight how dangerous this type of stereotyping can be, and that it is better to consider people as individuals with their own unique qualities.

Jealousy is another issue which can be explored, since Mhari wanted to believe that the Snoots were unkind and unloving people because she was envious of their possessions.

Simon's Story

CLASSROOM THEFT

Simon enjoyed going to Bradwell School most of the time, but he didn't like the days when he had a different teacher. This was because he was quite a shy boy and it took him a long time to decide whether or not he liked grown-up people.

His best friend was called Joe, and Simon loved it when they played football together. Joe would pass to him and he would pass to Joe, sometimes on the same team and sometimes against each other, trying to tackle and trip the other one up. Once he had hurt Joe in a tackle, but Joe was the kind of friend who didn't go off in a huff if things didn't go right.

Joe had even taught him how to play a Sega game so fast that he got onto a high level, but best of all Simon liked it when they sat next to each other in the playground and talked. My goodness, how they talked to each other! Joe would tell Simon about his Dad, even though he had never ever seen him.

'You see Si, I miss not having a Dad around, Mum's great, but she can't play footer and she wants me to be clean all the time. Dads don't want you to be clean all the time do they?'

Simon would agree and then tell Joe all about his Mum.

'Your Mum and my Dad ought to get together,' said Joe thoughtfully 'then we could both have a Mum and a Dad.'

So they sat for ages thinking of ways they could get Simon's

Dad to meet Joe's Mum, and they laughed and laughed at their crazy ideas.

Joe wasn't at school this week. He had had a sore throat and a stomach ache last week and he had been really tetchy and snappy – even with Simon. Then over the weekend the spots had started to show and he was told that he had chicken-pox. This left Simon at a bit of a loose end. He had never played with anyone else. He hadn't needed to because Joe was always around, and since he was so shy he now found it hard to ask other boys if he could play.

Playtime seemed very long, and lunch-break was even longer. He drifted round the playground only ever hovering on the edge of groups of children. Sometimes one of them would notice him and say something like 'What are you looking at?' and Simon would walk away to find another group.

As the week went on he grew sadder and more miserable, but on Thursday something terrible happened and Simon never really understood why. Lynzi Falkner had a pocketful of coins at snack time and she was showing off with them.

'I'll get aniseed twist with this one and chewy with this one . . . ' she said as she laid the coins out on the desk one by one. They were bright, sparkling coins and she moved them around with her long fingers.

'This one is for my juice and I've even enough for a new pencil.'

Simon watched the coins with their almost hypnotic gleam . . . and then it happened. One of the ten-pences flicked onto the floor and fell under the table. Lynzi bent down to pick it up and as she did, Simon slid his hand over the end coin on the table, lifted it and put it into his trouser pocket.

His heart raced as he edged away from Lynzi. His head beat wildly as he fidgeted with the rough edge of the disc in his pocket, and he looked quickly from one side of the room to the other. Nobody had noticed the coin had gone and he began to feel proud because he had managed to sneak a coin away right from underneath their noses. He almost laughed as he watched Lynzi still showing off to her friends.

'She can't even count,' he thought as he smiled to himself. 'She hasn't even seen that it's gone. Bet I can get it back on the table too,' he thought as the teacher walked in and he had to return to his place.

All morning he felt the coin as it pressed into his leg, or knocked against the table. He couldn't think properly because his mind kept flicking back to the coin. He had to touch it. He had to see it. He cupped it safely in his hand and felt every mark on it.

By lunch time he began to have doubts about getting the ten-pence back to Lynzi. In fact, he wasn't sure she should have it back, after all she had been showing off with it.

After lunch Simon found it a little easier to concentrate on a collage he was making with a group of three boys.

'Simon.' Miss Forman's voice suddenly echoed across the room and he visibly jumped.

'Simon, go and give Lynzi . . . '

'Oh, my goodness, she knows,' panicked Simon.

'a bit of a hand will you. She seems to be having some bother getting that glue open.'

Relieved, Simon went over to Lynzi.

'I'll help you,' he said, but he couldn't look at her eyes.

'Thanks Si,' said Lynzi.

'I think we need to run it under the tap. That usually does the trick.' Simon ran the neck of the bottle under the cold tap and worked the screw top loose enough for Lynzi to open it.

'Great Si. Thanks a lot,' she said.

'Simon!' Miss Forman's voice boomed across the room again. 'That was really kind of you.'

He went red. He found he couldn't look at Miss Forman either. He didn't want to look at anyone so instead he moved back to his group and carried on with the collage and he couldn't stop thinking about the coin.

On the way home, Simon was dawdling and kicking at dust that had gathered in the gutter and thinking long and hard about the events of the day. He was trying to square things in his own mind. Had he meant to steal or just to deceive, to be powerful or just have a joke? And no matter how hard he thought, the answer disappeared from view like the day-flies in this cloud of dust.

All of a sudden, he had the feeling that you get when you realise you are not alone and he turned quickly to find Lynzi only a step behind him.

'Hi there, Si,' she said in a quiet voice, no longer trying to show off.

'Watchya, Lynzi.' He tried to pull himself out of his deep thoughts and sound bright.

'You going straight home?'

'Yes, you too?' he asked with pretended interest.

'No, I'm going to the shop first. I'm going to get some chocolates for my sister. She likes them.'

Here it was again. Was she doing it deliberately? Did she know he had her ten-pence? No. She hadn't seen or she would have made a big fuss of it in class. Simon was sure she didn't know.

When they reached the shop she went inside and he wandered off towards his own home, quiet again with his own thoughts. But at the end of the street he turned and quickened his pace along Barlow Terrace eagerly looking for signs that somebody was at home at Joe's house.

He was lucky. Joe's front door stood a little open and he could hear Joe's Mum shouting up the stairs to his big sister Ellie. Simon knocked on the door and walked straight in as he usually did.

'Hi Val, can I see Joe please?' he asked, although he already knew the answer because Joe's Mum always let him into the house any time of day. She was good like that.

'He's in the garden, Simon. Ellie, time to lay the table,' she resumed her shouting up the stairs. Simon went straight to the back door and into the garden where he found Joe cuddling Ellie's rabbit. It was the biggest rabbit he had ever seen and it liked nothing better than to lie on its back like a baby and have the soles of its feet gently stroked. The two boys didn't greet each other. It never seemed necessary when they took each other's friendship almost for granted. Simon fondled the rabbit and then helped Joe to place the lumbering bundle back into the hutch.

'I cleaned it out yesterday too,' said Joe. 'There isn't much to do around here.'

'Why don't you get out the skateboard?' suggested Simon.

'Don't feel like it yet,' came the simple answer.

'You still feeling bad then?' asked Simon with concern.

'No, not really, just tired.' After that answer they settled down to that cozy silence that only friends can share.

After some time Joe broke the spell and asked if Simon had

been home yet or had his tea, and the answer 'no' surprised Joe quite a lot.

'Then why are you here now?'

'I don't know.'

'What do you mean by that?'

'I don't know a lot of things,' stated Simon miserably. 'Oh, Joe what am I going to do? I didn't mean to take Lynzi's money but I did, and now I really don't know . . . I don't know what to do at all,' and as Joe looked into Simon's unhappy face he could see the struggle in his eyes to hold back the tears.

'Tell us about it, Si.' And obediently Simon began to unfold the story of the coin in his pocket. Of course, Joe gave him good advice, but it wasn't what he wanted to hear. If he told Miss Forman he would get a long talking to. She might even send him along the corridor to Mr Peters' office, but worst of all she would probably make him cry. She had a way of doing that and he couldn't stand it. It was as if she saw right through him and knew all the answers to her questions before she asked them. He could never hide anything from her. She looked into his inside thoughts and that is what his mother used to do . . . and that always made him cry too. She never shouted at him, but always talked about being disappointed and let down, and somehow that was worse. There weren't many in the class who didn't care what Miss Forman thought about them, for she was someone you always wanted to please.

It wasn't any use arguing with Joe. He had asked his advice and got his answer and what made it worse was that Simon knew he was right. He knew what he had to do, so he left the garden, shouted cheerio to everyone as he walked through the house and back out of Joe's front door and headed for home.

Bully For You

BULLYING

Graham stared closely at the damp nostrils of his tiny guinea-pig, perfectly formed and only a few days old. They moved in time with each soft breath and they were velvet to the touch. He held the palest of the two piglets and cradled it next to his t-shirt. He could almost hear its breathing. It trusted him and gazed up with wonder in return. Graham sat with the guinea-pig for a long while, just thinking about the events of the day. He rubbed the back of his hand where a grey and pink mark, slightly raised and swollen, indicated the exact place where a freshly sharpened pencil had dug into his flesh. It was still painful when he touched it, but at least it no longer throbbed. He was very confused. Rory, who had dug the needle-sharp point of the pencil into his hand, had been his friend over the past week. Rory was quite new to the school and at first he seemed very popular. Lots of the boys had wanted to play with Rory and he was never short of somebody to play with, so it was quite flattering when he was asked to Rory's house after school. Graham had made a point of telling Steven Stockton. Now, of course, he understood why Steven had laughed.

At first there hadn't been anyone else in Rory's house. Graham had been looking forward to meeting Rory's parents and having a nice tea with cakes and everything. It hadn't worked out like that. Rory hadn't let him play with any games or the computer and he didn't have a back garden. They had watched television for the first hour or so.

'Do you want to go outside? Have you got a bike?' Graham had asked.

'No. I don't play outside,' replied Rory.

'Why not?' Graham wanted to know.

'Just don't,' and the conversation was clearly over.

After another programme on the television Graham ventured to try something else.

'Have you got any games in your room? Do you want to play something? There's not much else on now is there?'

'Just sit still,' snapped Rory, 'I'm watching.' And something in his voice began to warn Graham that this wasn't going the way he had expected.

'I think I shall go home now . . . ' but before he had finished, Rory's left arm shot out like an arrow and his hand slapped the side of Graham's face sharply with a stinging crack. At the same time Rory let out a high-pitched laugh and a smile lit up his eyes.

'Surprised you there. Come on, wrestle. Bet you can't wrestle.'

Graham didn't know what to do. His face stung and he was both angry and in pain, but Rory was laughing. It was clearly a joke. Obviously Rory didn't realise how much he had hurt him. It was an unlucky blow. Graham put on a brave smile in return, but he wasn't keen to play-fight with his cheek hot and glowing red.

'No. I really had better go. Mum said not to be too late,' began his excuses.

'Come on . . . ' squealed Rory as he lunged his whole body

across the settee at Graham who tried to move out of the way but only succeeded in catching his elbow on the edge of a coffee-table. Rory landed on top of him with his arms flying in all directions.

'Got you. Got you,' he laughed as blow after blow landed on Graham's neck and shoulders. He tried to protect his head by wrapping his arms around his forehead.

'Hi, boys!'

Rory stopped as quickly as he had started. Graham looked out across the tops of his own arms and saw an even larger version of Rory in the doorway. Rory got up and moved towards his brother. Seeing his chance to escape, Graham ran for the other door and found himself in the hallway. He fumbled at the front door lock with his heart pounding and his fingers twisting and turning the catch. To his complete amazement the door suddenly sprang open and a large lady stood blocking his pathway.

'Hello,' said the lady, but Graham pushed her backwards and she was forced to step aside as he leapt into the front garden and began the long run home.

That night, when he was in his bath, Graham's Mum had wanted to know what all the red marks were on his neck and upper arms. He made up a story about play-fighting, but he hadn't been really honest. He found that it was difficult to explain that his friend had thrown himself at him and had lashed out while he laughed and smiled.

During the week that followed, he tried to keep out of Rory's way. He noticed that Steven and Peter avoided sitting near Rory too and that they never chose him as a partner. They shuffled about if it looked like they were going to be told to join his group. Graham did the same and managed to keep out of Rory's way until Friday when he had to sit beside him for the News-circle. Whenever Miss Forman was paying attention to somebody else, Rory dug something sharp into Graham's knee. At first Graham couldn't work out how it was being done, and then he realised that there was some sort of sharp spike in Rory's pocket and that when his knee relaxed and went near the pocket, Rory poked the sharp spike through the material of his trousers. Whenever their eyes met, Rory would smile in a friendly manner, then as they were going back to their places, he jabbed the sharp-pointed pencil into the top of Graham's hand and moved off quickly to the other side of the room. It left Graham very confused as he sucked at the drops of blood on the back of his hand.

The Guinea-pig piglet in his arms wriggled and chirped. Graham had been standing for quite a long time and now the piglet was becoming anxious about being away from its mother for such a long time. Tenderly he replaced the piglet in the cage and then filled the water-bottle. After that he went into his house.

On Saturday Graham walked into the town to the pet shop. He did this every Saturday to buy sawdust and a bag of food for the guinea-pigs. Inside 'Everybody's Pets', Graham sat on the small stepladder in the corner and waited until Mrs Prentice had finished serving an elderly lady with budgie seed.

'Good morning, Graham. How's my laddo today?' she called across the old shop. 'Has your guinea piggled yet?'

Graham laughed. 'She had two and they're lovely. One is really dark with a patch of ginger on her eye and the other is nearly white. She's got one ginger foot.'

'How old?' asked Mrs. Prentice.

'She piggled on Sunday,' replied Graham.

'Nearly a week then. I've got a handful of Russian hamsters just in. Do you want to see?' Graham nodded. 'In the red cage Lovey. Get one out if you like.'

He spent a wonderful hour in the pet shop, finding out about the hamsters and listening to all the stories about the animals from the owners who popped in and out of the shop. Some of them were regular Saturday morning customers and they knew Graham well. Each of them was pleased to hear about his two new arrivals.

Eventually he left the shop carrying his large plastic bags, one filled with sawdust and the smaller one full of cereal for the guinea-pigs. He closed the door carefully and looked up. He came face to face with Rory. Rory had a smile on his lips.

'What's in the bags?' This was a silly question because he could see what was inside each one. 'Let's have a look then!' and Rory moved closer ... too close ... face to face ... breath on breath. There was no means of stepping out of his way. Rory's laughter was loud and it made him blink. His long finger ran down the food-bag and before Graham could tell him to stop, Rory ripped a hole in the bag. Dried pellets of coloured food cascaded onto the pavement. Graham quickly tried to reorganise the bags to stop the food falling out. Rory took advantage of this and sliced a larger hole in the sawdust bag. Flakes of wood-shavings began to drift into the road as Rory laughed.

Behind Graham the large shadow of Mrs Prentice appeared at the glass door, and when he saw this Rory shouted, 'See you!' and ran towards the High Street as Mrs Prentice opened the door.

'What on earth is going on here?' she said as she ushered Graham back into the shop. 'Who was that boy? I don't know him, do I?' she began. Graham was beginning to cry and luckily there were no customers in the shop.

'You just sit there Graham my laddo, and I'll get us both a cup of tea.' She handed him a tissue. Graham thought it had already been used, but he couldn't be bothered to mention it.

After a few minutes, Mrs Prentice came back into the shop with a tray of mugs and biscuits. 'Now, when you're ready, you tell me all about it, OK?' Graham nodded and sipped his tea. It was easy to talk to her. He liked her and he trusted her and they shared a love of all little animals, so he told her about Rory and his sudden attacks that threw him off-balance, and the high-pitched laughter. He told her about never being sure whether Rory was deliberately hurting him or getting carried away by accident. Apart from two interruptions, one customer for a flea-collar and the other for dog food, Graham managed to tell her everything and they had time to talk about it.

'Have you told anyone at school yet?'

'No,' answered Graham.

'Well, I don't see that you have any choice, do you? You see, Rory is going to carry on doing this until somebody stops him.' she advised.

'But then everyone will know I'm scared of him,' replied Graham.

'I think it sounds as if the other boys are scared of him too.'

'Yes they are.'

'Well, I think they'll be pleased when Rory is stopped. Then they won't be afraid either.' Graham thought about this for a while.

'Won't Rory beat me up if I tell on him?' he asked.

'I don't think so – not if the teacher handles it right. Kids like Rory always rely on everyone being too afraid of them to speak out. As long as it's a secret they think they can do anything, and it usually gets worse. Once it's out in the open and they know they are being watched, it usually stops. If not, the teacher can get Rory to leave the school, so he has to stop or else.' This sounded like good advice to Graham, so he asked,

'Why does he do it?'

'What, bully?'

Graham nodded.

'Well, bullies are often being bullied by someone else, or they can be really unhappy at home. There are lots of reasons. Sometimes they are jealous, or they don't have any confidence so they begin to boss the other kids and if they don't get stopped they can get really nasty. I tell you what Graham, if you can't talk to your teacher, then try your Grandad . . . anyone you can trust. Some kids don't have anyone to talk to so there are some help-lines that they can phone.'

'You know an awful lot, Mrs Prentice,' said Graham.

'Well, Graham, I read a lot of magazines when the shop is quiet. You can learn a lot from magazines. Now. Do you think that you can get home safely? Let's put that guinea-food in a fresh bag.'

'I think the sawdust has had it,' added Graham.

'Never mind, Lovey. Take yourself a fresh bag, OK?'

Graham thanked her for the new bags.

'See you next week Graham. Remember what I said.'

'Bye, Mrs Prentice.'

A Video Nasty

UNSUITABLE TELEVISION VIEWING

A chilling metallic sound rattled behind them . . . creek, crackle. Their hearts beat faster, breath-holding, pillow-clutching, and then the metallic rattling again . . . creek, crackle. It was the handle of the door. Neither of the girls could move or scream or think. A hand stretching into the room was lit by the green glow from the television and then . . . flick! click! . . . the lights went on.

'I thought you were in bed. What are you doing down here? Where's Jennifer?'

'Don't do that Mum!' sighed one of the girls who was stretched out on the floor.

'Don't do what?' asked her mum.

'Don't creep up on us like that.'

'Oh, you are just being silly. Where's Jennifer?' asked their mum. 'Jennifer's in the other room still doing her homework, I think,' the second girl replied. Their mother began to close the door behind herself as she left the room. Katie called out in a sudden panicking way,

'No Mum!'

'What is it? What's the matter?' her mum now became very concerned by the tone in her daughter's voice.

'Oh, nothing,' reassured Katie. 'Just leave the door open a little bit will you?'

'Yes all right. Come on now, it's time you were getting ready for bed anyway.'

Relieved that the door was still open and that the lights were left on, Katie and Lynzi began to tidy the videos into a neat pile. A quick press of the eject button whirred the last video slowly out of the machine and Katie put it back into its black plastic case and snapped it shut. They could hear the front door being opened and Mum's voice in the hall.

'Thanks again Jennifer. Are you sure they were no bother?'

'No problem at all Mrs Falkner. They were both as good as gold. Goodnight.'

'Goodnight. Just a minute. Is it all right for you to babysit on Friday this week?'

'Yes Mrs Falkner. About the same time?'

'Yes if you wouldn't mind.' Then the girls could hear the door being closed and the key being turned.

'Come on girls. Bed-time!'

Lynzi and Katie shared a bedroom. It was quite a large room, so instead of having bunk-beds, they had single ones at each end of the room. The dressing-table and toy-box stood in the middle so they were shared by the sisters. After washing and cleaning their teeth, they began to get changed into their night things. Lynzi always chose pyjamas whilst Katie preferred a long nightie. Tonight they seemed closer than ever to each other. They both used the bathroom together. They both went back to the bedroom together. Then when Lynzi returned to the bathroom, Katie followed her.

'Are you following me?' joked Lynzi. Katie quickly began to dry her hands on the towel.

'No,' she replied defensively. 'I just didn't wipe my hands properly that's all.' and since Lynzi had begun to move back towards the bedroom, Katie quickly followed behind her.

'You *are* following me!' she snapped.

'No I'm not. I'm just going to bed,' answered Katie.

Without any more conversation, both of the girls changed and got into bed. The central light was on, but each of the sisters put on their own bedside lights as well.

'Your turn to do the light,' said Lynzi casually.

'You're nearer,' said Katie.

'It's your turn,' complained Lynzi.

'Can't you do it for once?'

Suddenly the door opened fully and Mum stood in the doorway.

'Are you arguing now? What's the matter this time?'

'Lynzi won't do the light,' replied Katie.

'But it's her turn!'

'Oh! for goodness sake! What is it with you two tonight? Here. I'll do it. Now will you both get to sleep?' As the light went out the door was pulled to and their mum went out of the room. Lynzi stretched out her arm and switched off her side-light. Katie did not.

'Katie! Light!' Mum called and Katie reluctantly leaned across and switched off her own side-light. Both girls lay silently for quite a while. They heard the bathroom light click off, and saw the room go a little darker. Then the landing light was switched off and the room grew even darker still. Only the darkest shadows could be seen. Then their mother's bedroom light went out and the whole room suddenly became black dark with no shadows and no light.

After a while Katie whispered, 'Lynzi. Are you asleep?' But there was no reply, and she could tell from the steady breathing that Lynzi was already soundly asleep. Katie could not sleep. When she put her arm out of the bed she began to believe that something would touch it so she quickly withdrew it back under the covers and tucked them round her shoulders. Nothing was going to sneak into her bed! But it was too hot to have the covers pulled up around her neck. She wriggled and twisted and at one stage her leg was outside the covers too and she hastily drew it back in and curled into a ball. She didn't want to look at shadows so she screwed her eyes up tightly and it was like this that she fell asleep nearly half an hour later.

At three o'clock she woke up with a racing heartbeat, desperately needing the toilet. She reached out for the light switch, but suddenly, remembering the video that she had been watching that evening, she found she couldn't move. It was an awful feeling. The hairs on the back of her neck felt as if they were being brushed the wrong way. A shiver crept from the nape of her neck to a point just below her shoulder blades. She squeezed her toes tightly together.

'Lynzi, Lynzi, wake up. I need the toilet.' Lynzi snorted a little and changed position. 'Please Lynzi, please wake up. I need you.' Katie was almost sobbing. 'Lynzi . . . oh no!' She fumbled for the light switch and found it. She leapt out of bed and ran as quickly as she could into the bathroom. It was too late. The skirt part of her nightie was already wet. Mum appeared in the bathroom doorway.

'Are you all right, Petal?' she asked sleepily and then noticed the wet patch on the nightie. Katie's eyes filled with tears. 'Oh dear me, Love. Never mind. I'll find another one in the drawer.' And she disappeared into the bedroom to look for a clean nightie. When she pulled out Katie's favourite blue one, she was puzzled to find it damp. It didn't smell very nice either. The yellow one was the same. She turned round to find Katie standing behind her with rivers of tears running down her face.

'Oh, Katie, love. Why didn't you tell me?' Katie was too upset to be able to talk so her mother helped her to take off the wet nightie and put on clean pants and a vest.

'There. That will do for the moment.' Her mum pulled back the bedclothes to reveal a slightly damp sheet. 'You'd better sleep with me tonight. We can sort this out in the morning.' Her mum put out the light and held her hand as they went into her bedroom.

In the darkness Katie still held her mum's hand.

'Mum?'

'What?'

'I'm sorry.'

'It's OK. Why didn't you get up and go to the toilet?' she asked. Katie didn't answer straight away. After a few moments she replied, 'I was too scared.'

'What of? You were never scared of the dark as a baby. Why are you scared now?'

Again Katie took a long time to answer.

'Mum? Why is it that when I watch telly I'm not scared, but when I go to bed afterwards I *am* scared?'

'Well it depends on what you are watching. The children's programmes shouldn't be too scary. What have you been watching?' It was quite a while before Katie replied again.

'We watch videos,' she stated quietly.

'Which ones?' asked her mum.

'We watched *Deathwatch Two* tonight.'

'What? Where on earth did you get that from?'

'Jennifer brings them for us. They're always dead good,' answered Katie.

'But these videos are for adults, for grown-ups. Does she always bring videos when she baby-sits?'

'They are not always scary ones. She sometimes brings cartoons, but Lynzi likes the scary ones,' confided Katie.

'But Lynzi's older than you are, and anyway, some people scare easier than others. It depends on your imagination,' explained her mum.

'What's *imagination*?' asked Katie.

'Well, if you have a lot of imagination ... Oh dear, this is difficult to explain ... If you have a lot of imagination then videos can seem very real, and you tend to think about them a lot and you imagine that things are real even when the video is finished, so if, for example, your video was about monsters, then later you might think that your room is filled with monsters and it can be very frightening.'

'I think I've got a lot of imagination, Mum.'

'Perhaps you have at the moment, but you shouldn't have been watching an adult video in the first place. Jennifer should know better!'

'How can you tell if it's a grown-up's one or not?' asked Katie.

'All the videos have a code on them. There is a sign that lets you know. It says "U" if everyone can watch it, and "U.C." if it was made specially for children. But if it has got swearing or violence in it, or something frightening then it might have "P.G." on it and that means that parents have to decide whether or not to let their kids watch. I'll show you what I mean in the morning. We'll have a look at the boxes. Now. Do you think you and I could get a bit of sleep?'

'OK. Goodnight Mum.'

'Goodnight Petal.' Now that she felt safe and secure, Katie snuggled into her mother's arm and very soon was fast asleep.

Daredevils And Chickens

DANGEROUS GAMES

School was over for the day and the corridor was full of tumbling bodies all trying to put on their shoes and take coats off pegs. There were cries and nudges and then someone got hurt, for there was never enough room to manoeuvre school bags, shoes and children. Of course everyone wanted to be the first one out. There was more excitement than usual because today was Thursday, a fine, sunny Thursday, and most of the children were anticipating a chance, at last, to play outside in gardens or along pavements with friends.

Gradually the clusters of children began to move further towards the outer doors and classroom four fell silent – even Miss Forman had gone.

In the staffroom, several of the teachers were making coffee for themselves and sighing and sinking into the armchairs. Mr Peters was already in the room discussing a phonecall he had received from a very anxious lady who lived quite near the school.

'... and she said that he jumped straight into the road as if he hadn't seen the car at all.'

'I've heard of that game,' joined in Max Brown. 'Don't they call it chicken or custard or something like that?'

'Yes Max, I think you're right,' went on Mr. Peters 'but it could be a lethal game couldn't it?'

'Did the lady know who the children were?' Miss Forman was concerned already for a group of boys in her class that she knew were capable of playing such a game.

'Not all of them, Lesley. Robin Boyd's name was mentioned. She thought she recognised him, but there were at least two others.'

'Oh dear.' Miss Forman was now very concerned, 'I think I could guess who the other two were if Robin was with them. What would you like me to do? Have a talk with them and see if they will tell me about the game?'

'Yes Lesley, if you wouldn't mind, but I think I'll give one of my talks in Tuesday's assembly. We don't want something like this catching on with the younger ones. It's far too dangerous.'

They all agreed and Miss Forman began to turn over some ideas in her mind about how to tackle Robin and his friends.

On her way home, she decided to buy some peanuts for the birds but she drove slower than usual, suspicious that at any time one of her boys would pounce out between the parked cars that lined the edges of the high street. At the pelican crossing, a lady with a pushchair stepped off the kerb but Miss Forman was going slowly enough. No harm done, and the lady smiled in an apologetic way. Miss Forman drove off after the green light lit up.

Rounding the corner into the main shopping square, a policeman was holding up his arm stopping all traffic and diverting it along a narrow side street. Miss Forman managed to see a little of what was going on before being forced to turn, and she caught a glimpse of an ambulance as it pulled away from Safeway's car park. It didn't make her feel any more reassured about Robin and his friends.

On the local TV newsround the presenter spoke of an elderly lady who had lost her footing on the pavement in Safeway's car park at around five-thirty. Miss Forman was relieved and began to make the evening meal for herself and then she fed the cat. She realised that she had forgotten to buy the peanuts, but now that she was feeling a little easier, she settled down to mark the day's stack of jotters.

The spell of fine weather extended into the next morning. Although it was slightly frosty at seven o'clock, by the time Miss Forman left for work, the whiteness had gone off the grass and the sun was slightly dazzling as she headed into it on the way to school. She knew how to approach Robin and felt confident that he would tell her who his friends were.

Nearing the playing fields by the secondary school a small crowd of children were gathered round an old Metro car. She eyed them suspiciously. Cyclists seemed to dart out of nowhere today. Perhaps there were more of them? Maybe the sunny weather had brought the bikes out of their sheds for the first time this year? Children were crowding round a litter bin. Was Robin one of them?

After the unpleasant drive to the school Miss Forman walked towards the staffroom. She was greeted at the door by Max.

'Did you hear about Peter McDonald last night, Lesley?'

'No Max. What did I miss?' she answered, but although she had asked a question, she had guessed the answer and hoped to goodness she was wrong.

'He did that "chicken" thing. He was knocked down and I'm not sure, but I think he has a broken leg and has slight head injuries. They have taken him into the Infirmary but there's some talk of transferring him to the General.'

Miss Forman's heart froze. People were only transferred to the General Hospital if their condition was serious or they needed some specialised treatment that the local hospital couldn't provide. Leaving her tray of jotters and her coat, she made her way to the classroom and from the window scanned the playground for reliable children to question.

She spotted Robin hanging about the side entrance so she went outside to talk to him.

'Come into the classroom for a minute please, Robin. I need to talk to you.'

Quietly Robin was escorted into the room and she could tell from his expression that he had been involved in the accident.

'I've heard that Peter won't be in school today. Can you tell me why?' she asked calmly.

'Yes Miss,' came the reply.

'I'd like you to tell me about it so that I know what happened.'

Robin took a deep shuddering breath and began mechanically to retell the story. Miss Forman could tell from the way he spoke that he had had to tell and retell the story quite a few times. Probably the police had needed an account of what had happened. The ambulance crew, Peter's parents, and Robin's own parents would all have demanded an account of what happened. He would have been over the details again and again. ' . . . so Peter took his turn, and the next thing that came down the street was the TV repair van, but we said he had to do it anyway – even if it wasn't a car. So he jumped out into the road, but the van didn't stop and it threw him into Mrs Alsop's hedge, and he was all bleeding 'cos his head was cut. Bobby screamed and kept on screaming, but Peter didn't say a word at all. He just stared at me with big eyes and so I ran to get Mrs Alsop. The man got out of the van and he had a mobile phone and he was already phoning the police and then I was sick in a drain outside Mrs Alsop's.'

He came to an abrupt stop and Miss Forman wanted to put her arm round him and hold him tightly for the tears were streaming down his cheeks.

'I didn't do it on purpose Miss, honest I didn't. We all had a go. It was a real laugh Miss, and we all dared each other.'

'Well, Robin, I don't think you need me to tell you what a stupid game it was, do you?'

'No Miss.'

'Go and get a tissue and then maybe a quick wash will make you feel a little better. Hurry up before the bell goes.'

'Miss?'

'Yes what is it Robin?'

'Will you find out how he is for me?'

'Of course I will Robin. If I hear anything I'll let you know.'

'Thank you Miss.'

The Cat And The Slippers

BEREAVEMENT

George sat in his Nana's favourite room. He sat in her favourite chair. The material on the arm-rest was faded, and the wooden trim had been rubbed smooth. When he sat here, he felt closer to Nana than anywhere else in the house, although his legs weren't long enough for his feet to touch the floor. Her old grey cat came and sat where it used to sit, as close as it could to Nana's slippers, which still remained in their usual place beneath his dangling legs.

George didn't want to think about school, or bikes, or television when he came into Nana's room. Her funeral had been two days ago, and ever since they had got back home, his Dad had been trying to get him to go out on his bike to play with Graham or go for a ride in the car, but all he really wanted to do was sit in Nana's chair – in Nana's room.

He knew that she wasn't *his* Nana, she was his mother's Nana. That made her his great-grandmother. She had been a quiet, smiley kind of woman, and he could remember her laugh, because when she found something funny, her whole body seemed to move up and down with each rolling chuckle. She found lots of things funny – she sometimes found *him* funny. Recently he had been too big to sit on her lap, so they had held hands. He smiled as he thought of the crisp, thin papery skin on her hands, always cool to touch.

Suddenly the pictures in his mind disappeared as he heard footsteps. Graham Barclay arrived at his door and George jumped up.

'Coming outside?' asked Graham. George nodded, so they went downstairs and out into the garden. George found that when people were near him, he didn't think about the old lady that he had loved so much.

They played on their bikes for nearly an hour, going round and round the yard. George caught a glimpse of his Dad at the kitchen window watching, and he wanted to say,

'It's all right Dad, I'm quite happy playing with Graham. Don't worry about me.'

Graham stayed for tea. They had spaghetti bolognaise with grated cheese on top. Graham suddenly asked,

'Are you going to be at school tomorrow?'

George cast an eye at his mother and watched her carefully. She waited for him to answer.

'Yes,' he replied, then added quickly 'is that all right Mum?'

'Of course it's all right,' his mum answered. 'Do you want to?'

'Ahmm' was all the answer she got back, but she knew that this meant yes.

Graham went home shortly after tea and George went back up the stairs to sit on Nana's chair again. The memories leapt about his head and he let them in. He smiled when he thought about her special birthday surprise cake. Mum had bought it, but they had kept it a secret for two days, and he had made a card, and wrapped up some yellow roses from the garden, and Dad took some photos when they tip-toed into the room to give Nana her cake.

George sat just letting thoughts bubble up to the surface, like bubbles in a glass of lemonade. After half an hour he went downstairs.

The next morning seemed strange. Although he had only been away from school for three days, he felt as if he had been away for at least a couple of weeks. Mum put a note for Miss Forman in his bag. He knew that it told her that Nana had died, and that he had missed school because of the hospital visits and funeral.

'What about a packed lunch George?'

'Yes fine,' he replied absentmindedly as he spread more jam on his toast.

'OK. Time to go.'

The car was purring outside and Dad was going to drop him off at the school gate as he usually did on his way to work.

'Give me a kiss . . . Bye George. Have a nice day. See you Harry,' and she kissed his Dad on the cheek, just as she did every morning.

The drive to school was no different with the traffic lights on red as usual, and dad muttering something beside him. The lollipop lady let them through. Nothing had changed.

'But I feel different,' thought George.

In the High Street, and up at the Secondary school, he saw older children gathered in clusters. Nothing was new. Dad let him out at the school gates.

'See you tonight,' he called.

'Bye Dad.' Nothing new here either. The playground heaved with mingling noisy children. He found Graham and they walked together towards a group of boys jostling over a football. The bell rang.

He bought crisps at the tuck shop and put his packed lunch on the shelf which had been newly painted. It had a slightly sticky feel.

'Mmm. *That's* new,' thought George.

The morning passed very smoothly. He managed to do two pages in his workbook, instead of one, but that was the only difference. He hadn't missed much at all. He began to relax.

After the lunch-break all of the class sat on the floor to listen to instructions about the afternoon's activities. Miss Forman took a book from the table and began to read a story about a dog that had died and how the little boy was upset and he wanted to remember the dog, and he didn't want to bury it. As the children discussed the story George began to feel very angry. He watched them 'oo-ing' and 'ah-ing' and he knew that most of them didn't know what it was like to have someone die – *to have someone die!* – and to miss them and to worry about whether or not you would forget about the important things, like their smile, and their smell, and their voice.

'And anyway,' he thought, 'it's only a dog! You can't feel the same about a dog as I feel about Nana!'

Tears began welling up in his eyes, but they were angry tears. Miss Forman saw them. She quickly rounded off the talk and told everyone to draw a picture of something they loved very much. One by one the children took a piece of paper and went back to their own places. George couldn't move. He knew if he did that the tears would tumble out of his eyes, they were so full, and he couldn't see properly because they blurred everything into sparkling greyness.

He felt himself being led by the hand. He didn't resist. A tissue was placed in his hand and another began to dab at the wetness on his cheeks. But he was still angry.

'Nana wasn't a puppy-dog,' he said defiantly.

'I know George, but the feelings are a bit the same. The message in the story is the same,' replied Miss Forman.

'No it isn't,' continued George, 'you don't bury a Nana under an apple tree and put sticks on top. Nanas are too important for that.'

'But the little boy tried to remember all the good things about his dog, and you could try to remember the good things about your Nana.' Miss Forman hoped he would agree.

'I don't need to *try* to remember some good things,' stated George, 'I can remember hundreds of good things. I won't *ever* forget them.'

'That's great, but don't you worry that you *might* forget some of them at some time?'

George was reluctant to agree. 'Yes.'

In fact to be honest this was something he had already begun to worry about a lot.

'Well, the story is trying to show that we don't ever forget if it is important to us, so we don't need to go over our memory list every day. Just like the dog-lead reminded the little boy of the dog, and the basket, and the flattened ground in the garden where it used to curl up and sleep, so you will be reminded of your Nana by the little triggers, like someone's laugh that's almost the same, someone's wheelchair, a song perhaps, or the smell of her favourite flowers. These triggers will always remind you, just like opening a door in your memory. Memories get stored, they don't get forgotten.'

George looked at her for a few seconds. He didn't answer because he wanted to think about it.

'Do you want to draw something?' asked Miss Forman.

George nodded.

During the afternoon, George drew a large picture of a cat. As she watched the picture taking shape, Miss Forman was puzzled. She thought that George hadn't really understood what she had been trying to explain about the story.

When the bell rang at the end of the day, George put the picture carefully into his schoolbag and took it home.

In his bedroom, he slowly unfolded the paper and showed it to Nana's big grey cat.

'Here, Smokey! That's you!' he said to the cat who ignored him and continued to rub against his leg. 'And here are Nana's slippers. You can always be curled up next to Nana's slippers!'

George carefully put the picture and the slippers in a box he kept under the bed, stroked the cat, then went downstairs to play.

At The Bottom Of The Garden

SOLVENT ABUSE

For a while Joe felt light-headed, and then it seemed as if the floor was high up, somewhere where his head should be, and he was spinning. He put out his arms to stop himself falling any further, but his hands did not seem to be able to feel anything. He saw the sides of the garden shed cascading towards him. It was as if everything else was moving, and he was staying still. Then it went dark.

Mr Braithwaite heard the commotion in his garden as he was filling the kettle at the kitchen sink. He watched three boys come out of his old shed and stumble and fall round the end of his potato plot. One of them was crying as he ran into the strings of beans and became entangled. The other two scrambled over the hedge and zig-zagged down the alley that separated the gardens.

As he approached his shed, Mr Braithwaite heard moaning and he opened the door carefully, not sure what he would find. The fumes hit him at the entrance and made his eyes sting. On the floor, a boy was struggling to breathe, with sticky brown-coloured paste covering his mouth and part of his nose. Mr Braithwaite tried to clear some of the sticky glue with his handkerchief, but his hand became caught up with the toffee-like strands. He had never seen anything like it before.

In the darkness Joe heard voices.

'It's all right. You'll be all right . . . ,' a lady's voice kept repeating. Darkness again.

As he struggled to open his eyes, Joe saw lights, long bright lights which disappeared one after the other above his head. Something was across his face and down his throat. He felt sick, but he couldn't move. Suddenly, he *was* sick, but wasn't able to roll over in time to stop himself swallowing some of it and choking. Someone helped him to sit up a little bit and cleared the vomit from his mouth. He wanted to do this for himself but his arms wouldn't go where he wanted them to go. They seemed to flail wildly at the edges of his body until someone put them to rest by his sides.

He could hardly breathe. Something was stopping his breathing. It was on his face, smothering. He tried to grab at it but his hands didn't reach the mask before someone put them by his sides again.

'It's all right,' the voice said over and over again. 'You'll be all right.'

Worse than the suffocating mask was the panic he felt and the helplessness. His arms and legs didn't do what he told them. Lights sped past him, blurred and sparkling. It was like a nightmare. Then he felt the sharp needle of pain in his arm.

Shadows floated around him and he didn't know what they were. He wanted to hide.

'It's all right,' repeated the voice.

'No it's not!' he wanted to shout, 'It's not!' and then everything disappeared into blood-coloured darkness, and he slept.

When Joe woke up there was brilliant sunshine across his bed. Curtains were close beside him, but they weren't his curtains.

They had clowns on them. He didn't recognise them. He felt sick and then he fell asleep again.

This happened lots of times through the day. Once he thought he saw his mother's face, floating across the curtains. Anxious faces kept mingling with the brightly coloured juggling clowns. Joe was very frightened.

Gradually, more and more heads appeared, and some now had bodies attached and occasionally gloved hands drifted towards his face. Joe became aware of stinging sensations round his mouth and on his cheeks. The inside of his mouth and nose felt raw and were burning. He couldn't focus his eyes on anything for very long. They felt swollen and hot.

This was how Joe passed the day, drifting in and out of sleep, and the night followed the same pattern. He was frightened and lost. He tried to make sense of it all, and he tried to work out who was hurting him, but just when things were getting a little clearer the sleepy darkness would creep up on him.

The pale light of morning stole into the children's ward and Joe could hear crying and talking, clanking trolley-wheels and high-heeled shoes. Carefully, he opened his eyes and was relieved to be able to see quite clearly at last. He was tired and he ached, but he made an effort to move his arms and legs and was so pleased when they responded and went in the right direction. He began to realise that he was in a hospital, although he couldn't think why he should be in one. Slowly the images of the night came back to him and he shuddered at his thoughts. He wasn't sure what was real and what was nightmare.

'Oh, so you're awake now,' said the quiet lady's voice, 'How do you feel?'

Joe looked at the nurse who had just walked up to his bedside.

'Are you sore? Do you hurt now?' she asked.

Joe couldn't answer at first. His thoughts, his feelings, everything seemed to have slowed down.

'It's all right, take your time,' reassured the nurse.

Joe tried to ask what had happened, why he was lying in hospital and the nurse seemed to sense this and gave him the answers he wanted.

'You're in hospital, Joe. Do you remember how you and your friends were messing around with glue? It all went wrong. You nearly killed yourself.'

Joe thought for a while desperately trying to remember what he was doing before the floor came up and hit him and the walls of the garden shed caved in.

'You've been lucky Joe. The man whose shed you were in found you and called the ambulance. You're lucky he heard all the noise. Your friends had run away. If it wasn't for the old man you wouldn't be here now,' she continued.

Joe was confused as he tried to piece together the images of the shed, his friends, and the tubes of glue.

Up To Scratch

INFESTATIONS, HEAD LICE

Jasvinda was putting the last pieces of silver paper onto her space-rocket. She was very pleased with it. Nobody could tell that it had started life as a toilet roll tube and a washing-powder box. She turned to Bobby and with a laugh said,

'... and here's one I made earlier,' and she sat the rocket on the table next to his moon-buggy.

Miss Forman came across the room, and stood behind the children to admire their models.

'You have made a very good job of that Jasvinda. It's really lovely. Put it on the cupboard to dry off, and when Bobby is finished you can tidy up.'

Suddenly and unexpectedly, the rocket's wing began to bend and it started to topple off the table. Jasvinda moved quickly enough to stop it hitting the ground.

'That was close!' exclaimed Bobby.

Jasvinda remained crouching by the table legs while she looked at the damage to the rocket. Looking down on her, Miss Forman had spotted something else. On her black-brown glossy hair were the pale, almost white, tiny bobbles that had once been the egg-cases of lice. They were very close to the roots of her hair, so Miss Forman knew that Jasvinda had not had them for long. They looked like a sprinkling of round grains of salt.

Throughout the rest of the afternoon, Miss Forman, without being noticed, looked at the top of as many heads as she could. This was quite easy when the children were sitting down, and she found four more children with the tell-tale tiny white egg-cases sticking to their hair.

At the end of the day she told Mr Peters about her discovery of nits.

'There are at least four children who need to be checked,' she said.

'I'll phone the Medical Centre and ask if Mrs Watson can come pop along tomorrow and have a look at them all,' replied Mr Peters.

'I hope it's not like last time,' laughed Max, who was sitting in the corner of the staff room, 'when I called the nurse in and found that it wasn't nits at all. Some of the little monkeys had been playing at the park and had been throwing sand in each other's hair.'

'Never mind Max,' laughed Mr Peters, 'we still had to check.'

'Do you think the children are old enough to be told about nits and lice? I was thinking that if Mrs Watson had some information about how to prevent them, we could ask her to talk to the class. What do you think?' asked Miss Forman.

'Well,' hesitated Mr Peters, we usually only go into detail in their last year here, but I see no reason why they shouldn't learn about them sooner. The danger is, of course, that the parents don't usually like the others in the class to know if their son or daughter has nits.'

'Yes, but if all the children knew that nits prefer clean heads, and that any one can get them, then they are less likely to be silly or spiteful about it.'

'I see your point. OK, we'll try it out as an experiment and see how the children and parents react. And we'll see if it's easier to stamp out the infestations.' Mr Peters lifted the phone and arranged for Mrs Watson to call the next morning to find out how many children had nits in their hair.

When she arrived Mrs Watson had a carrier bag full of leaflets, and a roll of posters under her arm.

'Oh, I'm so glad you've decided to tell them all about head lice. You were lucky to catch me this week, I've been so busy. We've lots of infestations at the moment. I've brought a video with me too. Have you seen this one? It's very good. Now if you can send them to me a few at a time, I'll see how many are infested and we can send the letters home today.'

In her quiet bustling way, Mrs Watson took charge of the whole procedure. She gently looked at everybody's head before playtime. There were seven children with nits in their hair, four boys and three girls.

After playtime she went with Miss Forman to the class and began her talk.

'This is a picture of a louse. It's a sort of insect that lives in your hair. I'm going to tell you all about lice. Let's see if anyone knows anything about them first shall we? Who knows about lice?'

Nobody put their hand up, so she went on.

'Who would like to guess how big a louse is then? – anyone?'

Bobby put up his hand.

'This big?' he said using his hands to show something about the size of a mouse.

'My goodness me Bobby, I'm glad they're not *that* big. You wouldn't be able to put your hat on if they were *that* big.'

Sarita put up her hand.

'This big?' she questioned indicating something about the size of her thumbnail.

'No Sarita, not even that big. Lice are only the size of this.' and she held up a small match and pointed to the head of it. 'When they are fully grown they will not quite be as big as the top of this match, and they live on your head where it is warm. Which part of your hair is the warmest, the bit close to your head or the ends of your hair? Touch your hair and find out for yourself.'

All the children put their hands in their hair, and wriggled their fingers. Lynzi put her hand up,

'I think the hair next to my head is the warmest.'

'Absolutely right,' smiled Mrs Watson, 'and the little lice know that too, so they keep really close to the skin on your head to keep warm. They can't fly or jump, so they just spend their time crawling around eating and laying their eggs.'

'What do they eat?' interrupted Simon.

'They like the taste of your blood.' The whole class erupted with cries of 'yuk!' and 'ugh!'

'It's not very nice, but it's true,' went on Mrs Watson ignoring the squirming children. 'They like sucking blood from the top of your head.' She waited a little while for the children to settle down again. 'The mother louse lays about five, six, seven or sometimes eight skin-coloured eggs every night. They are skin-coloured so that you can't see them.'

'Camouflage!' exclaimed Daniel.

'Absolutely right,' replied Mrs Watson, 'and she is very clever because she makes a kind of gluey stuff, and sticks her eggs onto your hair, close to your head, so they can't fall off and you can hardly touch them with a comb.' She leaned back on her chair.

'How long do you think they take to hatch then?'

Hands shot up straight away.

'Bobby?'

'Half an hour.'

'No, longer than that. Jodie?'

'A year.'

'No far less than that. Do you know Steven?'

'A week.' he suggested.

'That's about right, somewhere between one and two weeks,' said Mrs Watson. 'They take just over a week to hatch. When the tiny eggshells are empty, they are still sticking to the hair, and remember, your hair is growing all the time, so eventually the empty egg shells start to show up on your hair. Most people's hair grows one centimetre a month.' She held up a small piece of string. 'This long each month. Can you all see? So if the egg shells are this far along each hair, I know that you have had lice for one month. That's four weeks. OK?'

Everyone nodded, and Mrs Watson continued. 'So, if I use a ruler, I can find out how long people have had their head lice for. Lice move very quickly, so you don't see many lice. When I check everyone's hair, it's the egg-shells that I check for. Does anyone know what kind of hair lice like best?'

Hands shot into the air again.

'Long hair.'

'Brown hair.'

'Curly hair.' came the flood of ideas.

'Wait a minute!' exclaimed Mrs Watson. 'I'll give you a clue. Dirty hair or clean hair?'

'Dirty hair,' came the quick reply.

'Well,' laughed the nurse, 'You are all wrong. Lice prefer clean hair. That's right,' she emphasised, 'Clean hair. And it doesn't really matter if your hair is long or short.'

The children looked surprised. They all thought that lice were dirty, and so that they would like to live in dirty, greasy hair.

'And, I'll tell you something else surprising,' continued Mrs Watson, 'they don't make everyone itch either, especially not at first. It can be months before you start to scratch. It's the juice in the louse's mouth that makes you itch, not the louse tickling you as it moves around.'

The children laughed.

'Well, I ought to tell you how you can avoid getting them, or how to get rid of them once you've got them. It's very easy indeed. Remember the lice have lots of legs. If it gets any of those legs knocked off, the louse will die, so how do you think you can knock a couple of its legs off?' Again an array of hands; 'Joe?'

'Hit your head!'

'I don't think so,' laughed Mrs Watson, 'it would be too sore.'

'Scratch your head,' offered Simon.

'Good idea, but that would hurt too much too after a while. Ben?'

'Wash your hair.'

'What a good idea, but I'm afraid that doesn't work either. I think I'll tell you – combing and brushing. That's all. Combing and brushing really thoroughly at night and in the morning is enough to make sure that the lice are injured and then these damaged lice can't lay more eggs and they die. Then you use a special lotion, I'll tell your mums and dads what lotion to get. If you put it on at night and then wash it off in the morning, it will kill off the adult lice that have survived the brushing as well. Who do you think you catch your lice from then?' asked Mrs Watson in her brisk matter-of-fact way. 'Your friends at school, or people in your family?'

The children thought for a moment then some chose their families while others suggested their friends.

'Well,' said the nurse, 'it's both really. They will move to anyone's head if it is close enough, and as I said before, they like clean hair best. So, if you have nits it is very likely that other people in your family will get them too, even grannies and grandpas.'

Then the nurse put on a video, so that they could watch pictures of magnified lice crawling through hair and find out exactly how to brush their hair to make sure that all the lice were damaged by the bristles of the brush.

At the end of the day the seven children who had been found to have nits were given a letter to explain to their mums and dads how to get rid of them and prevent catching them again. Everyone was given an information leaflet to take home too.

The next morning there were two mums waiting at the office when Miss Forman got to the school.

'Hey, you!' called out one of them as soon as she saw Miss Forman come through the entrance doors. 'What do you mean by this letter? How dare you accuse my son of having nits! He's not dirty! It'll be that Robinson kid he sits next to who has given them to him. I've never been so insulted in my life. Steven always gets washed at night. We've never had fleas before. I've a good mind to write a complaint.'

Miss Forman tried to interrupt. 'If you could just wait and see Mr Peters . . . '

'I've got no time to waste here. I've got to be at work in ten minutes. I've said what I came to say. Don't you dare to send another letter like this to my house.' She turned quickly and marched off to the main doors, letting them slam noisily as she went through.

Miss Forman moved towards the other mother who had been watching all of this and she tried to smile as she said,

'Can I help you?'

'Yes, actually I came to thank you for letting me know that Jasvinda had picked up nits. I hadn't noticed it, but I'd really like to thank you for telling the children that it doesn't mean they're dirty or uncared for and that it's so easy to stop it happening again. I asked Jasvinda what she knew about them and she has really understood very well, so thank you.'

Miss Forman was relieved that this second parent had not reacted in the same way as the first.

'I'm pleased that you appreciate what we are trying to do here,' she said.

'If I may suggest, Miss Forman, perhaps it is the *parents* who need to be educated about lice. I can see that some of them are very ignorant.' She smiled and said goodbye quietly and walked out of the main doors.

'I think you're right,' sighed Miss Forman to herself as she smiled and made her way to the class.

Slippery Snakes

SHOPLIFTING

An elderly lady pushed her wire basket against Danny's hip so he had no choice about moving nearer the pick-and-mix selection bar. The back of his neck felt hot and prickly and he thought all eyes were on him. He glanced towards the main entrance where the sliding doors were open since it was such a warm afternoon. He could see Blenco waiting outside leaning against the glass window with his hands in his pockets.

Danny took a deep breath and stretched out his hand so that he would grab as many jelly snakes as he could in one go. He would only get one chance.

'BING BONG! Would a checkout supervisor go to the main desk please? Checkout supervisor to the main desk. Thank you. BING BONG!'

Danny snatched his hand back and thrust it into his pocket. The shop's loud-speaker gave him such a surprise that he decided to make another tour round the store first. He moved to the video and C.D. area, rounded a display, and cruised down to the toys. He crossed the aisle and drifted into the hair and beauty section before walking back to the pick-and-mix bar as casually as he could.

Once more his heart began to pound.

'Grab the snakes,' Blenco had advised 'because they'll all lift up in a tangle and you'll get far more than if you grab at the wrapped toffees.'

Danny could see the shiny strands of coloured jelly. Again he spread out his hand as wide as it would go, took a deep breath and this time rammed his fingers into the tangled mess of sweet jelly snakes. He didn't look to see how many he had grabbed. He ran to the open doors in an attempt to get out of the shop as quickly as possible. Then everything seemed to get confused. A baby's buggy was blocking his path as he tried to cross the pedestrian precinct. He could see Blenco but he couldn't get to him. Each time he moved to get round one side of the buggy the stupid woman moved it the wrong way. This side! That side! Would she never get out of his way? He tried to jump over the front wheels, but his trainer got caught on the tyre and he stumbled forwards, wrapping a couple of slippery snakes over the baby's head as he fell. When he regained his balance, he looked up to see a large man in a brown security uniform looking down at him. The lady manoeuvred the buggy away and the man grabbed his arm.

'Hey, let me go, you . . . you . . .' cried Danny.

'I wouldn't do that if I were you,' said the man calmly. 'Let's go back in the shop for a little chat, shall we?'

'You can't do that!' protested Danny.

'Sorry to have to tell you this lad . . . but I can.'

Danny looked round the precinct but he couldn't see Blenco anywhere. The security guard led him through the doorway and back into the shop, holding his arm and forcing Danny to walk a little bit in front of him as he went. The big man picked up a trail of jelly snakes that must have fallen to the floor as Danny had made his dash for the doors. Now he felt that he was the centre of attention as the crowd of shoppers moved to let him through. Everyone seemed to be glaring at him with accusing eyes.

'You can't do this,' Danny kept repeating as they got nearer to the staircase at the back of the store. The security guard said nothing. They trudged up the stairs and stopped at a door marked 'Private' and the guard knocked on the door.

'Come in,' someone replied.

The guard opened the door and pushed Danny into the room.

'Thank you, Morrisey,' said a man in a suit who was sitting behind a huge desk. The security guard nodded and walked out of the room. The man put on his glasses before he spoke to Danny.

'Do you know why you have been brought to this office?'

Danny shook his head and stared at his hands. Of course he knew why, but somehow he couldn't say it.

'You were seen taking a large amount of confectionery from the sweet counter which we believe you did not intend to pay for. Is that right?'

Danny still could not answer because he was so stunned.

'Would you be good enough to empty your pockets, please?'

Danny did as he was asked . . . handkie, some money, half a pencil and a bundle of jelly snakes.

'Were you going to pay for these snakes? Think carefully before you reply and remember that that we have been taking a video of you.'

There was no use pretending that he had been going to pay. He could hardly say that he had lost his way to the cash desk and had run out of the shop by mistake. Miserably, he said, 'No.'

The man leant back in his seat.

'Well. We had better start with your name,' he said. Danny looked at him, absolutely horrified, but said nothing. The man took off his glasses and wearily rubbed his eyes.

'Let's start again, shall we? We need your name and address so that we can contact your parents . . . so . . . name?'

Oh, my goodness. Not his mum! Never in a million years did he think that his mum would ever find out.

The man leant forward to replace his glasses again and this sudden movement seemed to jolt Danny back to reality. He stammered,

'Danny.'

'That's better. Danny who?'

'Danny James Cohen.'

'Right. And what's your address, Danny?'

Danny found it hard to answer straight away. His mouth had gone very dry.

'Where do you live?' the man said in a patient manner. Danny told him his address but added,

'Mum'll not be there. She's at work.'

'Then you had better give us her work phone number as well.'

Oh, this was even worse. Mum hated being disturbed at work and having to leave the production line to answer the phone, but Danny felt he had no choice. He told the man her work number and the security guard left the room, presumably to phone.

'OK then. Which school do you go to?'

Danny told them.

'And Peter Blenkinsop . . . does he go to the same school?'

Danny nodded.

'And is he in the same class as you?'

'No he's older than me,' said Danny. He was trying to understand how they knew that Blenco had something to do with it. It didn't make sense.

'And you should have been at school today? It isn't a school holiday, I take it?'

The man was asking questions again.

'No. I should have been at school today,' said Danny, wishing that he were there right now.

'How long have you known Blenkinsop and been a friend of his?' asked the man.

'Just a couple of weeks, I think,' answered Danny. Suddenly he felt himself panic.

'I've never done it before. Never!' he shouted. 'I'll never do it again, I promise.'

The man gave no reaction to this sudden outburst, but went on with his next question.

'How old are you?'

Danny could not cope any longer and he began to cry. He heard the door open behind him and he turned to look at the security guard who walked in. Danny could hear himself gasp for air between sobs.

'What have I done?' he kept saying to himself, 'what have I done?'

The guard came over to talk to him.

'The police have contacted your mother and she says she'll be here in about ten minutes. We'll just wait for her, shall we?'

Then he turned to the manager behind the desk, 'The police say one of their officers can get here in a few minutes.'

Danny felt miserable.

It took a quarter of an hour for his mum to leave work and get to the town centre. All in all, the interview with the manager and the police took another hour. Mum warned Danny to tell the truth about everything. She told him it was very serious.

They didn't talk to each other on the way home. Every time his mum looked at him, Danny felt wretched and turned away. Once inside the house, Danny ran upstairs and lay on his bed crying. His mum didn't follow him upstairs as she normally would have done if she thought he was upset. He felt so alone, and so sorry for himself and angry at the same time.

It seemed like ages before his mum eventually came into his room. She was carrying two cups of tea. Danny turned away from her and faced the wall. He was so ashamed.

'I've brought you a cup of tea,' she said. 'I think it's about time you and I did some talking.'

At the sound of her voice Danny knew the only thing he wanted was a cuddle from his mum. He rolled over and buried his face in her lap, snuggling as close as he could. Then she asked him the one question he couldn't answer.

'Why, Danny?'

When she got no reply, she carried on talking.

'You've never gone short of sweets. I know we don't have a lot of spare money, but you've never gone short of sweets.' She was gently stroking his hair. 'Was it the danger?'

'Danger?' he asked.

'Yes. Did it excite you, the thought that you might get caught?' she explained.

'No. Not really. Blenco said I wouldn't get caught,' said Danny. He wanted to explain to his mum so he continued 'He made it sound so exciting, Mum, and he said we'd never get caught. I didn't think about what would happen. I didn't even think it was bad, really – just a few ten-pence snakes, that's all.' Danny looked away.

'You're in a lot of trouble Danny, but we'll face the music together, as long as you are honest with me from now on,' said his mum.

'I'm sorry. I'm so sorry,' said Danny.

'I had a talk with the policeman,' continued his mum, 'and he said they have been trying to catch Blenco for quite a while. It seems that he does the same thing most Thursday afternoons. Each time he uses a different boy and a different shop. He shows the younger boys how to steal things. The police have caught three of them so far, but Blenco always stays outside the shop and disappears as soon as there is any trouble.'

'Will they catch him?' asked Danny.

'Yes, quite soon, and when they do, he's in for big trouble,' replied his mum.

'But he doesn't do any stealing,' explained Danny.

'That doesn't matter. What he is doing is called "aiding and abetting". He is training boys to steal for him. That's against the law.'

'Could he go to prison?' asked Danny.

'No. He wouldn't go to prison, but he might get a police warning. It doesn't sound like much but it's still serious – a bit like starting a criminal record, and the police will watch him very carefully after that.'

'Mum?' asked Danny with tears in his eyes, 'Will I have a criminal record?'

'Well, Danny, I'm not sure yet. I don't know enough about it, but we have to go to the police station next week and the sergeant will talk to you about it. But, like I say, we will face the music together.'

The next morning Danny and his mum went to school together. She talked to Mr Peters about everything that had happened ... staying off school, stealing, being caught ... she left nothing out. Danny sat on the edge of the chair and squirmed. He was so ashamed that he wished he could vanish, but he couldn't. He told the truth, as his mum had asked him. He said he was sorry, and he really was.

When he was allowed to go back to his classroom he didn't want to talk to anyone. He told nobody about his terrible Thursday afternoon.

Before lunch he was sent to the office with the register. He spotted Blenco through the glass classroom door. Their eyes met and then Blenco turned his head away as if Danny meant absolutely nothing to him.

At home he tried hard to please his mum. He didn't ask for any special treats, like staying up late or having a video from the shop. He even had a go at washing up for her. He desperately wanted to prove that he could behave himself.

They went to the police station together and Danny found out that he was just a little bit too young for an official police warning, but that didn't stop the sergeant giving him a really good telling off. He also had to explain how Blenco had taught him and then the whole story was written down and he had to sign his name at the end of it.

Gradually over the next few weeks, the bad memories of the

shoplifting began to fade, but they were brought sharply back into focus again when he heard Miss Forman's comment one Thursday afternoon.

'Does anyone know where Joe is this afternoon? No? That's funny. He seemed all right this morning.'

Danny wondered where Blenco was on this Thursday afternoon, and if Joe was in a shop right now risking all that trouble . . . and what for? A handful of slippery snakes!

Pass It On

EXTORTION

Rain ran in drizzles down the window, each droplet collecting and connecting with the others as it ran from the top of the pane to the bottom. Miss Forman looked up from Thomas' book and thought,

'Oh, no. Not another wet playtime.'

The children working in the library corner looked up and thought,

'Oh, no. Not another wet playtime.'

A tall boy from the senior class stood at the doorway and knocked on the wooden panelling and handed a note to Miss Forman, confirming what she already knew. Officially, and this note from Mr Peters proved it, it was yet another wet playtime.

'Let me remind you of the class rules,' began Miss Forman as she started to explain, again, which equipment could be played with and which could not.

'Wet playtime comics are in that tray, but please put them back tidily afterwards,' and she ran through the whole routine as she had done yesterday and the day before. The children didn't like being indoors, and she didn't want to keep them in, but the weather had been so miserably wet for the past fortnight that there was no way that they could go out even for a short time.

As they settled down to their chosen activities and began to eat their snack, she noticed a sudden and carefully concealed movement as Ben went past Brien. It was such an unusual sort of movement, and all that really happened was that Brien gave something to Ben, but what was really odd was the way in which it had been a sly move, a hidden move, and the speed at which Ben had moved on.

Miss Forman stood watching for a while but nothing else happened so she went to the staffroom for a much needed cup of tea.

The bell rang. It was a piercing sound and most unwelcome at the end of breaktime, and as Miss Forman walked across the dinner hall towards the classroom her heart sank as she saw the group of senior monitors waiting at the entrance, for this was a sure sign that there had been trouble during playtime. The monitors all tried to talk at once.

'Ben was fighting with Kevin.'

'Kevin was hitting Ben really hard, Miss.' She could already see that this was going to take a long time to sort out, but after ten minutes of questions she was no further forward. The boys apologised to each other but neither of them seemed genuinely sorry. Ben's eyes remained stormy and Kevin's eyes stayed cast down as if looking for squashed crisps on the carpet.

The rest of the morning passed fairly smoothly and the rain faded to a slight drizzle by the time dinners had been served and so at last everyone could go outside to play. Miss Forman had gone to the staffroom for lunch, and only returned to the classroom for a few books she had forgotten. The trouble was that they were in one of the top cupboards and so she had to stand on a chair to reach. She lifted two books on dinosaurs and another about lizards and she was ready to climb down, but on turning to get down again she found that this high view-point allowed her to see out of the window and over the top of the ornamental hedge that separated the infant and senior playgrounds. Ben was standing by the hedge with his hands on his hips and his head held high. Then Kevin appeared, as if he had been bending down, and he handed something to Ben. Without smiling, Ben ran to the guard-rail that surrounded the whole school and gave something to two secondary school boys and then one of them hit Ben very sharply in the stomach. Quickly, both boys moved away, leaving Ben standing alone. After a few moments he, too, moved off and headed for the school. Since he didn't seem seriously hurt, Miss Forman decided to wait for him to come into school and tell her about the big boys. She would then be able to find out who they were and phone their school so that they could be interviewed over there.

For some reason, Ben didn't mention anything about the incident at all. The afternoon passed quietly and he didn't really seem bothered about his lunch-time thumping at all. In fact, it was Kevin who seemed upset and almost ready to cry.

Next day was Thursday and Kevin was no happier. At last it was a dry playtime and Kevin made a quick dash to the cloakroom as soon as his table were allowed to go out. Yet, at the end of playtime he was again quiet and subdued in his line waiting to go in. Amanda Cherry's eyes were red and runny looking.

'Are you all right, Amanda?' asked Miss Forman.

'Yes,' mumbled Amanda, but Miss Forman wasn't convinced and although she didn't know exactly what had upset Amanda, she began to feel that something was very wrong. If only she could work out what it was.

At the end of the afternoon a note arrived from the headteacher and Miss Forman read it quickly while listening to the red reading group. There had been a phone-call from Mrs Philips, Kevin's mother, asking for a chance to speak after school.

As the final bell rang at the end of the day, Miss Forman made her way to the office to see if Mrs Philips had arrived and found both Mr and Mrs Philips already waiting.

'Sorry to keep you,' she began.

'That's no problem,' Mr Philips replied, but he did not smile. 'I hope you did not mind us coming in at such short notice, but we were beginning to get very worried. We think we have a bit of a problem with Kevin.' he continued.

'Yes,' interrupted Mrs Philips, 'and we wondered if you could give us any advice . . . '

'Well, I will if I can,' answered Miss Forman.

'You see, for the past couple of weeks or so my wife and I have had this funny feeling that money was going missing, you know the sort of thing? We'd put left over change on the mantelpiece and when we came to get it, it wasn't there.'

'We weren't sure at first, because in our house Jack and I just tend to leave money about and if one of us needs it, we just use it. So I always thought Jack was moving the money, and he always thought it was me.'

'Not a great lot of money, mind you,' said Mr Philips 'usually the change out of my pockets and such, but it did seem odd that suddenly there were no coins or notes left around. But, then our Jennifer's money-box key went missing for a week and when she did get the thing opened there was only about half of what there should have been.' Mr Philips stopped talking and sat back in the chair but his wife continued.

'But more seriously, today I knew I had a pound coin in my purse as well as a five pound note. When I got to the shop there was only the fiver! I know I wasn't mistaken about that. I know it must have gone this morning and I know the only person who could have taken it was Kevin.'

'Aye. I'm sorry to say we think our Kevin is a thief and we are worried sick in case he is doing the same thing at school,' concluded Mr Philips.

As Miss Forman listened, the jig-saw puzzle of feelings she had felt all week began to fall into place.

'Thank you for coming in to tell me,' she began 'Do you think you could leave things for a day or two and do nothing more about it?' The two parents looked at each other. 'You see,' went on Miss Forman, 'I have an idea that if Kevin is taking money, then it is not for himself. Have you seen him with lots of toys or books, extra sweets and things that you didn't buy him?'

'No. I can't say that I have,' replied Kevin's father.

'Nor have I, Mr Philips. But I do know that he is a very unhappy little boy at the moment and if you could leave this with me for a day or so, I think I could find out not only if he is taking the money, but why he is doing it. In the meantime, do you think you could go on leaving a few odd pence around as you would normally do?' and Miss Forman continued to explain what she expected to happen and Kevin's parents understood and agreed to go along with the plan.

They didn't have long to wait because the next day seemed to follow the same pattern. Kevin, unhappy and sullen, reluctantly went into the playground at lunchtime. Miss Forman put the chair against the cupboard door and stood on it to try and get a good view over the ornamental hedge between the two playgrounds. Then she waited. Just as before, she saw the two secondary school boys at the railings when Ben and Kevin were beside the hedge. Kevin handed something to Ben, who took it straight to the older boys. In turn, they held Ben by the edges of his V-neck sweater and then pushed him away. He ran back towards the school building. But also, as part of the plan, the deputy head of the secondary school appeared on the path, near the railings. From her high position, Miss Forman could see him talking to the two boys and then walk with them towards the secondary school. At the same time, Mr Peters walked through the swing doors with Kevin and Ben marching in front of him.

'I think,' said Mr Peters 'that I will interview Ben while you talk to Kevin. I think there is a lot they want to tell us, don't you Miss Forman?'

The boys looked down at their feet.

'I Can't Breathe'

ASTHMA

First thing in the morning there was no snow at all. The grass was green and the tarmac was black and dry. Then, just as the first bell of the day rang out across the playing fields, small flakes of snow began to fall here and there across the playground, and they stayed where they landed – not melting away – just lying.

As soon as they got into the classroom, Miss Forman's children knew they had to get changed for P.E. straight away. It was always a rush on Tuesdays – no time to take dinner money, or buy anything from the tuck shop. There was only time for a quick head count, and then straight into the hall where Mrs Johnstone was putting out the mats.

Philip and Jamail were the last ones to go into the hall. Jamail couldn't do up his new trainers. What had appeared easy when the shop assistant fastened them, was now proving to be more complicated than he had bargained for, and he was affronted when Miss Forman had to help him.

'These are stiff,' she remarked. 'The straps won't bend will they?' she continued while at the same time pushing and pulling his foot into the left shoe. She winced as her finger nail caught in the plastic lace-hole and tore off. Once in the hall he joined the others running on the spot, hopping, bending and stretching until they were all puffing and warm. Mrs Johnstone clapped her hands and they gathered around her for their next set of instructions. It sounded like fun. The hall was laid out like a miniature assault course, with skittles, benches, ropes and bean bags all strategically placed and ready to be crawled along, balanced along and kicked. Everyone waited for the signal to start, and then they were off. Jamail and Philip began with the step-ups. They went slowly at first and then began to pick up speed, looking at each other to see who was going the fastest. Philip smiled, he thought he was the best, but then Jamail put his head down and went as fast as he could. Step up, up step down, down. He was concentrating so hard that he didn't even notice that Philip had given up until the signal from Mrs Johnstone told them all to stop. Philip was bending over trying to catch his breath. Jamail slapped him playfully on the back as he ran to join the main group again. Philip didn't move.

'Just wait here a minute,' said Mrs Johnstone as she went across to Philip. 'Everything all right?' she asked.

'I . . . can't . . . breathe,' gasped Philip.

'Have you got your inhaler?' She knew that Philip sometimes needed his inhaler when P.E. triggered off his asthma.

' . . . In . . . the . . . Office,' he gasped.

'OK.' She turned towards the rest of the class. 'Jamail, will you go and ask Miss Forman for Philip's inhaler? The rest of you just relax for a few moments, and Jodie, will you get a chair from over there? Thank you.'

Jodie did as she was asked, finding a small chair from the wet area nearest to the classroom. Jamail ran back to the class to find Miss Forman taking down their display of 'Things that Fly'.

'Miss Forman,' he panted, 'Philip needs his inhaler.'

'Oh, right. I'll bring it.' She climbed down from the chair she had been standing on, and handed him a box of drawing pins. 'Pop these on my desk please.'

Then she walked out of the room towards the Main Office. Jamail placed the box carefully on her table and then returned to the hall.

'She's gone to get it.' He told Mrs Johnstone who was holding Philip's hand.

The children were waiting patiently and were talking quietly amongst themselves. Miss Forman arrived carrying a small carton and Jamail watched closely, even though Mrs Johnstone was giving the class the next set of instructions.

Jamail saw how Miss Forman talked quietly to Philip and she held his hand. He looked white and upset and his breathing was quick and fluttery. He saw her take the inhaler out of its carton and give it a good shake and all the time she smiled and talked calmly to Philip. He saw her reminding him to breathe out first and Philip nod to show that he understood, and then he put the end of the inhaler into his mouth and pressed the silver canister. Jamail noticed the way Philip's chest rose as he inhaled the medicine. He did this twice.

'Jamail! Don't day-dream. Catch up with your group, quickly.' Mrs Johnstone's voice interrupted his thoughts, and he got up and ran to the far end of the hall to begin football dribbling round skittles.

By playtime the snow was falling in a steady cascade like somebody sprinkling a pillowful of feathers out of the clouds. The grass was completely white and the tarmac was turning grey. The youngest children had to stay inside for a wet playtime, but the older ones were given a choice and most of them wanted to play outside. There wasn't enough snow for snowballing so they ran around in crazy zig-zags trying to catch the flakes in their mouths as they swirled around the buildings.

Philip had chosen to stay in, but everyone else had elected to go out, to enjoy the snow.

In the staff room, the teachers were not so overjoyed to see the steadily falling flakes.

'I've phoned the AA and the Regional Weather Station and they both agree that there is worse snow to follow this afternoon. It's coming from the East and is already causing chaos on the M4 so I have decided to send the children home as soon as possible.' Mr Peters was addressing his emergency staff meeting.

'The bus company has already arranged with the secondary school to uplift all the bus children at twelve-thirty and to concentrate on getting the pupils from the outlying areas home first. This will mean an earlier lunch-break for us, but Miss Green says there's no problem in the kitchen and she thinks we can start lunches at about ten to twelve.'

Everyone nodded their understanding.

'Joyce is already phoning round parents and emergency contacts to see how many children will have someone at home or can be collected, and that seems to be going OK so far. She'll bring a list to each of you so that you know which children can go at twelve-thirty and which ones will have to stay.'

Nobody disagreed. It was the usual procedure for closing the school early. Mrs Johnstone spoke first.

'Do you want me to carry on with the P.E. before dinner?'

'Right,' said Mr Peters thoughtfully, 'you'll have to stop at eleven-thirty so that the tables can be put out for lunches, so there isn't really a lot of time left for you to take a class. Which class were you getting next?'

Mr Brown groaned, 'It was mine.'

'Right,' said Mr Peters again, clearly trying to think things out in his mind before making a decision. 'I think you should take Maureen's class instead so she can get home – she has furthest to go.'

'Thanks a lot,' replied Maureen.

'Any more questions?' asked Mr Peters. There was no reply. Everyone looked at each other trying to think of something they might have forgotten, but it all seemed pretty straightforward.

By the end of playtime the snow was very heavy and the wind was driving it into little heaps in the corners of the doorways. Once in the classroom after playing outside the children were all very excited. It was obvious now that the snow was here to stay, at least until home time, and they were planning what they could do with it. The rest of the morning dragged on and each time a little squall of wind sent the snow hurling in blizzard-like conditions, the children became even more boisterous and excited.

Eventually, the list of names from the office arrived and arrangements had been made for everyone to get to their own home, or their grandparents', or a neighbour's. Parents were always good about this, offering to take children who couldn't get home because both mum and dad were working.

Jamail's mum offered to walk with Philip to his house because his mum couldn't get away from the factory until her shift finished at quarter to one. Jamail's mum made sure that both boys were wrapped up tightly with their scarves wound round their faces.

She asked, 'Have you got everything boys? Schoolbag? Hats?'

'Yes. Let's go Mum. I want to get home and play in it.'

She laughed. 'I don't think you'll want to play in the snow once you see what it's like out there. I've never seen anything like it, and it's so cold.'

Miss Forman approached the boys with her list.

'Mrs Singh, you're taking Jamail and Philip, yes?'

'Yes. Philip's mum thinks she'll get back to her house just about the same time that we do. We're only up the road a little, so if she doesn't arrive at that time, I told her I'd keep Philip at my house, just to be safe,' replied Jamail's mum.

'That's awfully good of you, Mrs Singh. Thank you very much for helping out.'

'It's no problem. We'll set off now. Ready boys?'

'Ready Mum! Come on,' said Jamail impatiently. He had plans for snowballs and igloos. He couldn't wait.

Once they got outside and moved away from the shelter of the school buildings he was surprised by the fierce knife-edge of the wind. It blew through the material of his trousers and stung the back of his knees. He turned his face away from the hard icy pellets of snow that had picked up speed as they were hurled across the playing fields. The snow was only a few centimetres deep but it was a struggle to keep walking because the gusts of wind whipped against his whole body, and despite having his thickest coat on, Jamail felt very cold. The snow looked like a moving sea of white coming towards him and it hardly rested on the ground before it was chased upwards again by the wind.

Philip was holding his scarf in place around his face trying to stop the stinging pellets of snow from hitting him. He, too, was finding it difficult to keep going.

'Here, give me your bag,' said Mrs Singh as she lifted it from his shoulders. She could see that both boys were finding it a struggle.

They marched on for another five minutes or so. The snow was clinging to their woolly hats and their trouser legs as they walked across the railway bridge and down towards the high street. Philip was beginning to fall behind Jamail.

'Keep together boys,' commanded Mrs Singh as she stretched out a sheltering arm.

'Got . . . to . . . stop!' panted Philip as he drew to a halt and bent over, holding onto his knees for support.

'What's wrong, Philip?' asked Mrs Singh as she walked back to him, but he didn't answer. His face had gone white and he was gasping in short shallow breaths.

'He needs his inhaler,' Jamail replied for him. 'I think it's his asthma.' Mrs Singh looked at her son.

'What do we do?' she asked him.

'Have you got your inhaler?' he asked Philip, and in reply Philip pointed to his school-bag.

'We'll move to that doorway,' stated Jamail who seemed to have taken control of the situation, and the three of them moved slowly to the shelter of a shop doorway. Mrs Singh supported Philip, and Jamail carried all of the bags.

'It's the . . . cold . . . ,' Philip was trying to explain.

'It's all right,' said Jamail, 'don't talk. I know what to do. He took Philip's hand and placed it in his mother's large woolly mittened hands. Then he began to rummage in the schoolbag for the inhaler. Philip was becoming worried.

'It's . . . in . . . there. I think . . . it . . . is . . . I'm sure it's in . . . there.' Words were coming huskily on top of the shallow breaths.

'It's OK. I know it's in here,' said Jamail as calmly as he could, all the time his fingers searching the corners and pockets of the bag. It wasn't easy with his thick snow-dusted gloves so he pulled one of them off and continued his search.

'It won't take a moment. Just relax.' He tried to keep his voice calm, but he was getting worried until at last he felt the corners of the carton. He took the inhaler out of its box and shook it, just as he had seen Miss Forman doing that morning.

'You know how to do this yourself, don't you. I'll help you a little bit. Breathe right out,' he instructed Philip, who nodded and exhaled, took hold of the inhaler and pressed the end. There was a gassy hissing noise like an air-freshener as Philip breathed deeply. Then he repeated the procedure. Jamail took the inhaler from him and put it back in its box, and replaced that in the schoolbag.

The three of them sheltered in the doorway for a few more minutes.

Philip's colour had come back and he was breathing more deeply and he smiled at Jamail and his mum.

'Are you all right now?' asked Mrs Singh anxiously, 'Do you think we should try to get you home?'

'Yes, I'll be OK now. Thanks.' Philip beamed a big 'thank you' smile at Jamail who grinned back.

They picked up their bags again and adjusted their coats around their necks. Mrs Singh took Philip's hand and the three of them set off again like Arctic explorers.

When they got home, Jamail's mum asked him,

'When did you learn all that about looking after somebody with asthma? You were really impressive there.'

Jamail had actually impressed himself, being so calm and in control, trying to make Philip relax, but he said,

'Don't know. It's just something I picked up at school,' and he glided casually past on his way to the kitchen.

Mrs Singh was left wondering if Jamail had the makings of a doctor.

'Doctor Singh,' she thought. There had never been a doctor in her family before. She quite liked the idea.

The Risk

SMOKING

'It might be the Easter holidays, but some people still have to work. The world doesn't stop just because it's Easter.'

Lucy sensed that it was no use complaining. She had heard the lecture before. Her mum was one of those people who always seemed to have to work when everyone else was on holiday. It was the same at Christmas, and then at New Year. Now she had to work over Easter and it just wasn't fair. Her mum saw her expression and softened a little.

'Lucy, I *need* this job. I *like* this job. The only thing I don't like about it is having to work through the holidays.'

'I know, Mum. I just wished that we got *our* holidays like everyone else,' said Lucy.

'Oh, Lucy. When you're young, you think that everybody has a holiday at the same time, but they don't, you know. What would happen if all the policemen and the firemen had their holidays on the same days? Or the doctors and nurses?' explained her mum.

Lucy had heard the arguments before and it did make sense, but she still resented the fact that it was Bank Holiday and her mum had to work.

'And who,' her mum continued, 'who do you think is going to make meals at Mainsrigg if I don't turn up? Now go and get ready, there's a good girl – and tell Calum to get a move on too.'

Although Lucy was still unhappy, she got up from the sofa and went upstairs. She yelled at Calum's closed door.

'Going in five minutes,' and then she stormed into her own bedroom. Hearing no reply, she stormed out again and burst into Calum's room, but he wasn't there. She stood for a moment wondering where he could be, and then she stomped her way downstairs and out of the back door. She had a good idea where he was. She crept across the lawn because it made less noise than the gravel path, and then she tip-toed up to the old shed. The window was propped open with a chunk of wood since it had no real latch. It was a bit too high up for Lucy to see through so she took a piece of stick and knocked the chunk of wood out of position, letting the window clatter against it's old frame.

Calum shot out of the shed door, slammed it shut and leant against it. Then he roared at Lucy.

'Jees, Lucy! What do you think you're playing at? What a stupid thing to do.' She had obviously given him a fright.

'Did you think it was Mum?' she said smugly. He didn't answer.

'A message for you,' she continued, 'Going in five minutes,' and she turned and ran up the path, quite pleased with herself. She knew where to find him, and she knew what he was doing.

Calum didn't move straight away. He had thought that he'd been caught. He breathed deeply and went back into the shed. He placed the cigarette packet under the largest plant pot in the pile and used the step-ladder to put the matches on a high shelf. He pulled open an old drawer and took a mint out of a small tin. Then he opened the door, went out sucking the mint and then bolted the door behind him. He exhaled a lot of breath into his cupped hands and smelt it, and decided that he couldn't smell the cigarette smoke at all.

All the way to Mainsrigg, Lucy kept grinning at him with a knowing look in her eye. Calum made an effort to ignore her and eventually gave up. Mum parked in her usual place in the car park and they all went into the old people's home through the back door. Mum made her way straight into the kitchen, giving the children instructions on the way.

'Don't make a lot of noise! Don't get under anyone's feet, and if you do go off to the park let me know first, and don't be late for your lunch. With a bit of luck we could be cleared up and away from here by about three o'clock. OK?' She didn't wait for an answer, after all, they knew the routine and they were good kids. They wouldn't get into any bother. She began putting on her apron and went to the menu sheets to remind herself what she had promised to cook them all for their Easter Monday lunch.

Calum and Lucy walked into the main lounge to see who was up and dressed. One of the auxiliaries saw them as they arrived.

'Hello you two. What are you up to today?' she asked while trying to help Mr Graham get to his feet. Calum saw that she was having to struggle, so he went over to help.

'Nothing much,' he replied as he moved the Zimmer-frame in front of the old man so that he could lean on it.

The auxiliary said, 'Thanks Calum. I'm sure Mr Graham gets heavier every day. Isn't that right?' she shouted at the old man, 'You get heavier every day!' Mr Graham just smiled as he began his slow walk down the length of the lounge.

'Deaf as a post!' she remarked to Calum, but Calum wasn't so sure. He felt that Mr Graham heard a lot, but said little.

Lucy had disappeared into the television room. She usually did. Calum thought he would find someone who would give him a game of dominoes. He looked round the room, but two of the elderly women were dozing.

Sister McRae came bustling into the lounge. He liked her because she always made him laugh.

'Good morning Calum. What are you after?'

'Well, I thought I'd have a game of dominoes or something, but there's nobody here who'll give me a game, is there?'

Sister McRae looked round the lounge and pulled a face.

'Hmm. Quieter than a turkey at Christmas in here!'

Calum laughed.

'You might have more luck in the conservatory. I saw Mr Thomson heading off that way. I think he was going to water the azaleas or something.'

'Right-o,' said Calum and he set off along the main corridor that led to the conservatory and there, as Sister McRae had predicted, was Mr Thomson holding a watering-can.

'Hi,' said Calum as he bounced into one of the soft wicker chairs.

'Hello Calum. And how are you this morning?' asked Mr Thomson as he put down the watering-can.

'Fine thanks,' replied Calum.

'Mum working today?' Mr Thomson added, and then realised that it was a silly question. Calum wouldn't be there unless his mum were working. He corrected himself quietly. 'Course she is. 'Course she is. Silly old fool.' Then he spoke louder to Calum. 'It'll be a good dinner then. Any ideas? Chicken? Fish?'

Calum smiled. 'Egg and bacon pie.'

'Yummy-yum! Your mum makes the best pies I've tasted since my Lizzie made them.' He moved a chair closer to Calum and sat down.

'Do you fancy dominoes, Mr Thomson?' asked Calum.

'Not today, thanks son.'

Calum was about to moan when he remembered that Mr Thomson had days when he really didn't feel too well. Instead, they sat for a few moments in silence. Mr Thomson sniffed a couple of times.

'Mints don't quite hide it, you know,' he said. Calum's eyes widened, but Mr Thomson went on, 'Lizzie used to think they did. She tried lavender-water as well, but I could always tell.' He looked directly at Calum. 'Still can!'

They continued to sit for some minutes. Calum would have got up to leave if he could have thought of a good excuse.

Suddenly Mr Thomson said, 'Cough was the first sign, you know. Every night, every morning. Hack. Hack. Hack.' It was as if he were talking to someone else in the room now. '"Give 'em up, Lizzie," I'd say to her. "Whatever do you mean?" she would answer. But I knew. Hack. Hack. Hack. Cough. Cough. Cough.'

He looked at his hands for a while.

'She started in the forces, you know,' he suddenly resumed the conversation. 'Of course, they were handed out to all the troops then. Doctors thought cigarettes calmed your nerves then, you see. Calmed my Lizzie all right!' he added bitterly. 'She thought I didn't know, but you can't disguise the smell. She had breath like an ash-tray some days – a bit like yours today!'

Calum reddened and began to get out of the chair.

'Don't take offence, son, eh? Try listening to one who knows and who's seen it.'

Reluctantly, Calum leaned back in the chair.

'You've been smoking for a few weeks now, haven't you?' stated Mr Thomson.

'How do you know?' asked Calum suspiciously.

'I can tell, son. I smell it on your clothes and your hair and on your breath. Oh! I can smell the mints too. I'll never forget the smell of the smoke, son. Never.'

This amazed Calum as his mum hadn't noticed any smell – or she would have had plenty to say about it.

'I expect you'll say that lots of people smoke and they don't all get lung cancer, won't you?'

Calum didn't answer. It was almost word for word what Peter had said to him when he had given him his first cigarette.

'Of course, *she* didn't die of lung cancer. Heart attack!' He paused and gazed into the distance 'That was after she had the thrombosis in her leg and had it amputated ... cut off ... and then there were five – or was it six – years confined to her bed.' Again he looked at Calum. 'It wasn't quick at all.'

Calum felt very uncomfortable. He wanted to go home.

Lucy burst into the conservatory.

'Oh, here you are. Hello Mr Thomson,' she exclaimed.

'Hello, Lucy. Come for a game of dominoes, have you?' He turned to Calum. 'Better find where Sister McRae keeps them.'

They spent a good hour playing together, then enjoyed their lunch. Mr Thomson never said another word about Lizzie, or smoking, and neither did Calum.

Campfire Story

TRAVELLING PEOPLE

The flames from the fire made sticks crackle and sparks jump into the air. The piece of beechwood smouldered and smelt like a delicious mixture of fresh moss and smoked kippers. All around the campsite people were moving, talking and laughing. Dogs sat quietly as near to the fire as they dared to go . . . almost singeing. The smell of damp dog hung in the air.

Clemmie sat on the caravan steps with her head resting against the hinges of the open door. She loved this particular site. It was near the river, so it tended to have a clinging dampness all through the early Spring, but then, it was sheltered by a small wood on two sides, which calmed the biting April wind. Later in the Summer it was like a sun-trap. Yes, it was her favourite site, just on the outskirts of Bradwell. Although many travellers liked to move freely throughout the Summer months, her family chose to stay in this one place. The annual horse fair each May was a wonderful sight and her father did most of his earning in May, selling young foals that had been reared through the Winter on the moorland down South. They really only migrated between the two sites now. Years ago her grandfather and grandmother had travelled up and down the country, staying on maybe six or seven different camps each year, meeting up with friends and family and going wherever there was a better site and an opportunity to earn. Nowadays there were fewer good places to stay and Clemmie's father said that the two camps were enough. It suited him.

Her brother, Nathan, made his way across to the caravan bringing her a can of cola and a packet of crisps.

'Here you are,' he said, throwing the crisps into her lap. Then studying her face he asked, 'Are you decided then?'

She thought for a moment before replying and then said, 'I'm going.'

Nathan shook his head. 'I'm not!' he stated.

'Well, I'll go and pack then,' said Clemmie and she stood up.

'Why, Clemmie? You'd be much better off staying away,' Nathan began to argue.

'I told you. I like it at school. I like being able to read and I like being able to do numbers,' she replied.

'Pa can teach you numbers and I'll teach you a bit of the reading. You don't have to go to the school.' He was beginning to become angry, but Clemmie was not going to change her mind. She kept her voice steady.

'I like going to school Nathan. There's more than just adding up numbers you know, and I can read better than you already. And anyway, I want to see my friends again ... so I'm going!'

'Oh, have it your own way! You'll be sorry,' he said sulkily. 'No good ever came of schooling.' He spun round and stormed off across the site and disappeared into the shadows.

'Poor Nathan,' thought Clemmie. He never had liked school and now, at thirteen, Pa had given up trying to get him an education. She had always wanted to go to school. She couldn't get to one near the South campsite because it was too high up on the moors and far too difficult to travel to, but it was different on the Bradwell site. She could walk to the school by herself.

Clemmie went to the caravan and looked in her storage box for her schoolbag. She took it out and shook it, to clear off any dust. She searched in her cupboards and on the shelves for her pencils and pens and put the ones she could find into the bag. She reached under her pillow and drew out an exercise book that was so full there were even loose papers stuffed among its pages. She looked at the book with pride, felt the edges and flicked the corner, letting the pages tumble together. She was proud of her work. It was time, she decided, time for someone to see it. Quickly she put the book inside her bag and zipped it shut.

Clemmie made herself two tuna sandwiches and put those, with the packet of crisps from Nathan, into a plastic box. Now she was ready to start school again in the morning. She could hardly wait and later, in bed, she was almost too excited to sleep. Eventually she slept, still holding her bag where it rested on top of her bed.

There was no need for an alarm clock in the caravan. The dogs barked at daybreak and the women got up to stir up the fires, cook breakfast and boil water for the tea. Clemmie, who was always a light sleeper, woke up with the sound of the dogs and the smell of the rekindled wood. She washed and dressed herself and then her mum appeared at the door with a lovely hot mug of tea and a bacon sandwich. There was a galley-style kitchen in the van and a cooker that ran on bottled gas, but her mum preferred to cook in the open when she could.

'You ready then?' asked her mum.

'Nearly,' Clemmie replied, 'I've got my shoes to clean and my teeth to do. Is my hair OK?'

Her mother looked at the shiny black hair that fell into natural ringlets.

'You look lovely,' she said 'but wait a minute.' She opened a small cupboard drawer and brought out a length of dark red velvet ribbon. 'Would you like to tie it into a pony-tail with this? It would keep it tidier.' Clemmie thought that the ribbon was beautiful and her mum helped her tie back most of her hair. It was thick and curly and whisps of it kept escaping, but most of it was caught and held by the ribbon. Then her mum brushed her shoes while she cleaned her teeth.

'Ready now!' she said as her dad walked into the caravan.

'That you ready for the off? I'll give you a lift down in the wagon,' he said and so Clemmie drove down to the school in the lorry that her dad used for pulling the caravan, and they arrived before most of the other children were in the playground. Her dad walked with her to the secretary's office. He knew the way.

'Good mornin'', he said to Mrs Barrie.

'Hello. Can I help you?' she replied.

'I'm here to enrol the girl,' he said, then realised that she was not the same secretary that he had seen before. He had a good memory for faces.

'Ah. You'll be new here,' he remarked and then said more helpfully, 'Travelling People. Form T 4 A. She used to keep them in the middle drawer of the filing cabinet,' he pointed, 'that one!'

Mrs Barrie was a little surprised to be told where to find the appropriate enrolment forms and was relieved when Mr Peters walked in.

'Ah. Mr Peters. How are you? I hope you are keeping well, Sir.'

'Well, hello Mr . . . Mr . . .?'

'Corning. Michael Corning.'

'Yes of course it is, but I haven't forgotten your name, Clemmie. How are you?'

'I'm very well thank you Mr Peters,' replied Clemmie.

'Good, good. You're here to enrol again I take it?' inquired Mr Peters.

'That's so. Clemmie likes the heducation and so do I,' said Mr Corning. 'I'm all for the heducation.'

Mrs Barrie had found the forms and she handed them to the headteacher.

'Then there shouldn't be any problems,' he said as he took them. 'How long do you expect to stay this time?'

'Well, I dare say about the same as last year, give or take a week. It depends on the trading and the weather as always,' replied Mr Corning.

'Good. Good.'

They spent some time filling in the forms and talking about the winter and how Nathan was doing, and then Clemmie was introduced to Miss Forman. Clemmie was given a tray and a desk in her new classroom. Although she didn't know her teacher or the layout of the room, she did know the children because she joined the same class every year.

'I think there's time for you to go out and play, Clemmie. See if you can find any of your friends out there. Come back if you have any problems,' suggested Miss Forman, and Clemmie eagerly ran out into the playground.

She recognised Simon, Jasvinda and Joe straight away. Miss

Forman watched from the window as the children greeted each other and Clemmie was immediately accepted by the group.

'You shouldn't have any trouble, Lesley,' said Mr Peters. 'Clemmie spends almost five months here each year and the class is used to that now. She's actually made a lot of friends.'

'Does she go to any other schools?' asked Miss Forman.

'No, but amazingly enough, she manages to keep up. Language work is really good, and she reads a lot. She'll probably need to see Max for some extra help with maths though. She tends to fall behind with that much more than language. She's had help from Max before so she knows what to expect. I'll go and see if he can timetable her in,' said Mr Peters and he left the classroom. Miss Forman only had time to find a few essentials for Clemmie . . . a jotter, a workbook and some activity sheets . . . and then the bell went.

Clemmie was so pleased to be at school. She felt she was lucky with the class she joined each year. For a start it was the same class every time and that gave her a chance to get to know the children very well, and they never thought of her as odd or different any more. She knew that it wasn't like this for all travelling children. She had heard of awful things happening to other travellers when they tried to go to school – like being called names, having things thrown at them, and being drawn into fights. No. Clemmie felt really lucky to have found Bradwell School.

At lunchtime she ate her sandwiches and swapped crisps with Jasvinda and Simon. She made them laugh with campfire stories, like how a cat chased her dog up a tree and it got stuck. There was so much to talk about.

By the end of the day Clemmie was very tired, but happy. She collected her things together ready to go home, and remembered the exercise book she had brought with her. She hung back a little when the bell rang, not leaving with the first battalion of children charging out of the door. She waited until there was just herself and Miss Forman left in the room.

'Hello, Clemmie. Are you waiting to be collected?' asked her teacher.

'No. I wondered . . . do you think you could have a look at this?' She bent down and unzipped her bag, brought out the book and presented it to Miss Forman.

'You've been busy! Did you do this on your own?'

Clemmie drew near, pleased that someone was showing an interest in her treasured writing. 'Yes. I began writing it like a diary, but then I began to make things up. It made it more imaginative. Most of it isn't really true. What do you think?' She looked at Miss Forman excitedly.

'I'd like to have time to read it through, properly, if that's all right with you. It looks fascinating. When do you do your writing?' she asked.

Clemmie replied 'I write mostly in the winter – at least that's how it began, but now I find that I write all the time.'

'Well, Clemmie, I think I'll enjoy reading this. I'll take it home and then we can talk about it in a couple of days. Is that OK?'

Clemmie beamed. 'That'd be great,' and she picked up her bag and left the classroom.

Outside the air was quite chilly, with enough sunshine left in the afternoon to suggest that spring was starting. Clemmie pulled her jacket collar around her neck and walked briskly towards the bridle path that would take her to the caravan site. She hadn't quite reached the bridle path when she became aware of someone close behind her, and, thinking that she was blocking the way, she stepped aside and turned to see who was so desperate to overtake her. Before she realised what was happening, she was pushed into a prickly hawthorn hedge and a boy grabbed her collar, thrusting his face right up to hers. She could smell his foul breath.

'We don't like you! We don't want you! Tell your lot to clear off. Tell 'em to go!' and he spat at her face. She felt the sharp barbs of the hawthorn as they cut through her jacket, and she tried to lean forward so that she could avoid the thorns but the boy pushed her deeper into the hedging.

'We don't want Gypsies like you. You're stupid. Do you get it girl? D'you understand?' He was becoming more and more aggressive as he spoke. He swung his foot in a half-hearted kick, and then he did it again . . . only harder. And then again, harder still. Clemmie closed her eyes so that she didn't have to watch his face, but suddenly she felt him moving quickly away from her. She opened her eyes to see Simon and Jasvinda dragging at the boy's arms and neck. Realising that he couldn't tackle three children at once, the boy twisted and turned until he was free and then able to run away.

Jasvinda began to untangle the mass of curly hair that was caught in the hawthorn hedge. Simon tried to help. At that moment a car drew up and Mr Peters got out and ran to the children.

'Are you all right?'

'It's OK Sir,' replied Simon. 'I know who it was.'

'Clemmie, are you all right?' Mr Peters asked.

Clemmie was still dazed and didn't answer. Most of her hair was free but it was in a terrible tangled mess. She pulled at the last lengths of it by herself but when she saw the state it was in, she began to cry.

'It's all right Clemmie. You'll be all right now,' comforted Jasvinda.

'I think it would be best if I took you the rest of the way home, Clemmie. What about you two?' Mr Peters turned and asked Simon and Jasvinda, then considered for a moment. 'I think I'll take you home as well, just to see that you get home safely.' He was worried that the boy might still be around somewhere.

'Thank you Sir,' said Simon.

The children got in the car and Jasvinda put her arm around Clemmie who was still shaking. She looked greyish white and she clung onto Simon's arm.

At the caravan site Mr Peters got out of the car and began asking a group of young men where he could find Mr Corning, but before he had finished, he saw him striding across the site.

'Mr Corning. I'm sorry. Clemmie's had some bother with a boy from the secondary school. She's OK but she's had a fright.'

Mr Corning ran to the car and lifted Clemmie out and held her in his arms while she sobbed.

'Sh, now, sh, now,' he crooned. Then speaking directly to Mr Peters he said, 'You'd better come into the van.'

Mr Peters went into the caravan while Simon and Jasvinda stayed in the car.

'I'll have to be quick as I still have those two to take home.' He pointed to the other two children. He told Clemmie's parents what had happened and at the end of the account Mr Corning was furious.

'Well! That's an end to her heducation. No more schooling,' he stated.

'Oh, no. Please don't stop her coming to school,' said Mr Peters. 'There's no trouble in the school itself. It's getting to and from it that looks as if it might be a problem. Have a think about it, Mr Corning. I can see you're upset, and rightly so, but think about it overnight and come and see me in the morning. Now I'm sorry, I have to go. These children's parents will start to worry if I don't get them home soon.'

'Aye, all right,' said Mr Corning. 'I'll talk with you in the morning.'

Mr Peters left the site and took Simon and Jasvinda home, explaining to their families why they were late and how proud he was of the way in which they had helped Clemmie.

The next morning, Clemmie and her dad were waiting at the office when Mr Peters arrived.

'Hello there, Mr Peters, Sir,' hailed Mr Corning. 'I am delivering my daughter to you, personally, for her heducation.' Clemmie beamed at him.

'I'm pleased about that,' replied Mr Peters, 'In fact, I've just been hearing from Miss Forman what a gifted young girl you have, Mr Corning.'

'I'm also grateful to you for returning Clemmie safely home to us yesterday.' Mr Corning held out a pair of freshly caught brown trout. 'By way of a "thank you"' he said.

'Well,' said Mr Peters, surprised by the gift, 'how could I possibly refuse?'

'And,' continued Mr Corning, 'a special "thank you" to Simon and Jasvinda.' He produced from his pocket a length of green velvet ribbon and a small, carved wooden aeroplane.

'I think the *girl* would be best having the ribbon, don't you?' and he winked as he placed the gifts in the hands of the surprised Mr Peters, and then left the office, leaving Clemmie at school . . . to finish her heducation.

Nadine's New Baby

A BABY SIBLING

The doorbell rang and Nadine opened it. Auntie Christine stood beaming on the doorstep and didn't wait to be invited in. She swept passed Nadine and began to take her coat off in the hall.

'You hang that up for me, there's a good little girl,' said Auntie Christine as she folded her coat and handed it to Nadine. Aunt Christine swept like a tornado into the sitting-room exclaiming, 'Is he in here?' as she went.

This wasn't Auntie Christine's usual entrance. She *usually* half lifted Nadine off the floor with her hug and kiss routine. She *usually* said words like 'Poppet' and 'Pipsqueak.' She had never ever called her a 'good little girl.'

Nadine couldn't hang the coat up. She wasn't tall enough, so she left it on a chair beside the coat-stand and followed Auntie Christine into the sitting-room, only to be brushed aside as Auntie Christine whirled out again.

'Why didn't you tell me he wasn't in there? Where is he?'

'Daddy?'

'No, Silly-Billy,' snapped Auntie Christine shortly. 'Samuel!'

'I think Mummy took him up for a sleep,' said Nadine, bewildered. The tornado began to wind itself up the stairs towards the bedroom. Nadine followed out of curiosity.

'Linda! Who's a clever girl then?' crooned Auntie Christine as she folded Nadine's mummy in a huge hug.

'Oh, Christine!' said her mummy excitedly 'Come and look.'

All the bluster and noise seemed to seep out of the tornado as she leant over the edge of the cot and looked down at the tiny face of the new baby.

'He's lovely,' she whispered and her voice was all soft and gentle. 'Is he good?' she asked.

'Yes he is,' Nadine's mummy replied.

'He's beautiful . . . just wonderful,' and they stared at the baby for ages. Nadine wondered what they were looking for. Then the doorbell rang.

'Can you get that Nadine?' called her mummy.

Nadine went back down the stairs to the hall and opened the front door. It was Nana and Grandpa Roberts. They had come to visit every day that week. Nana made lovely teas, like scrambled eggs, spaghetti hoops or bacon sandwiches. Grandpa always played games after tea and even helped to dress her dolls.

'Hello, Mugwump!' he said as he half squeezed her to death in one of his bear hugs. 'How are you today?' Then, as if they shared a secret, he added, 'How's the Grumbleweed?'

She knew what he meant. 'He's up in his cot.'

'Still grumbling?'

'Only sometimes,' she replied.

'Who's coat is that?' asked Nana. Nothing went unnoticed by her eagle eyes.

'Auntie Christine's,' said Nadine.

'Well, you'd have thought a grown woman could have hung up

her coat properly, wouldn't you?' she said as she shook the coat straight and then hung it on a peg. 'But that's Christine for you!' and Nana walked through to the kitchen.

'How long has Auntie Christine been here?' asked Grandpa.

'She's only just got here,' answered Nadine. He groaned and held out his hand and they walked into the sitting-room.

In front of the fire was a baby bath, half full of cooling water. A few bubbles still clung to the edges. The floor was littered with all the baby things . . . changing mat, powder, a nearly full pack of elasticated nappies, bottom cream, dirty baby-grow, and a dribbled-on matinee jacket. Grandpa began to tidy up.

'Come on, Mugwump, give me a hand with this will you?'

Nadine was getting used to the routine. She held the door open and Grandpa carried the baby bath carefully through so that he could empty it in the kitchen. They put the top on the bottom cream, pressed the lid on the baby shampoo, lifted the dirty clothes and dropped them in the linen basket behind the settee.

'We're lucky, Mugwump,' said Grandpa. Nadine stopped.

'Lucky?' she asked.

'Yes,' chuckled Grandpa, 'no smellies.'

She burst out laughing. No dirty nappy to put in the bucket, thank goodness, although she did enjoy the performance Grandpa made of carrying the offending nappy while pinching his nose and making the most hideous faces.

Nana brought in a tray of juice and biscuits. There was also coffee for Grandpa.

'There now,' she said automatically as she put the tray on a small table. 'Have you tidied up for Mummy? Oh, you are a good wee thing. Now have your juice and do your reading for

Grandpa before tea,' and she swept out of the room without expecting an answer.

They drank coffee and juice in silence and Nadine nibbled round the edge of her chocolate biscuit.

'Well then, let's do the reading.' Grandpa looked round the room for Nadine's school-bag.

'Can we do it later?' she asked.

'If you like, Mugwump, if you like,' said Grandpa, thoughtfully. It was unusual for Nadine to delay her reading because she loved it so much.

They sat for a while longer without talking, and then Nadine said, 'Grandpa?'

'What is it Precious?'

'Grandpa, why do babies have so much junk?'

'Well,' Grandpa answered slowly, 'does he really have any more than you?'

Nadine considered this.

'Samuel has a bath, clothes, towels, talc, bottles, nappies, . . . lots of things,' was her answer.

'You have a bath, toys, clothes and towels too. You have a lot of food in the fridge,' suggested Grandpa.

'But Samuel's things are all round the sitting-room. My bath is in the bathroom and I share that too.' Grandpa could tell from her tone of voice that she wasn't happy about this, so he tried to explain.

'I think it's because Mummy hasn't sorted out where to put all his things yet. You aren't pleased with his things in the sitting-room then?'

'No,' argued Nadine, 'If I left all my stuff in here Daddy would get really cross. He'd make me tidy it all up before I could go to bed.'

'Ah!' sighed Grandpa. 'That's the difference, isn't it?'

'What?' she asked.

'Samuel is too tiny to do anything for himself yet, isn't he? He has to have everything done for him. He can't tidy up.'

'He takes up all Mummy's time.'

'Ah!' sighed Grandpa again in a knowing way.

'She doesn't do my reading with me anymore and people keep calling in to see Samuel and then they have a cup of tea and she talks to them. Then they go home and she feeds Samuel, and then someone else calls.'

Grandpa put his arm around her shoulders and Nadine leaned against him.

'I'm afraid it's going to be like that for a bit,' he said.

'Why?'

'Well there are so many things that can go wrong with a baby, so when one is born fine and healthy like Samuel, everyone gets very excited. Everyone likes to see who he looks like. Women tend to go all gooey and seem to fall in love with babies at first sight,' he chuckled, 'I don't know why.'

'Did they go all gooey over me when I was a baby?' asked Nadine.

'More than ever, Mugwump. You were incredibly beautiful and everyone was thrilled because the doctors thought Mummy wouldn't be able to have babies, so you were extra special. You wouldn't believe the fuss they made over you!'

'Samuel doesn't make *me* go all gooey.'

'No, I don't suppose he does. I don't suppose you really like him all that much, do you?'

'No, not really.'

'Don't worry. Babies grow on you. After a while you'll see that they can be fun, and then, when he's bigger, he can even be your best friend.'

'Really?' Nadine wanted to believe him.

'Yes, Mugwump. Now, where is that reading?' Grandpa began searching in his jacket pocket for his glasses.

'Grandpa?' asked Nadine. 'Can we do the reading later?' Grandpa eyed Nadine suspiciously.

'OK,' he said. 'What's wrong?' Nadine was about to say 'nothing' when she changed her mind. She went to her school-bag behind the chair and opened it, pulled out the bookbag that held her word cards and her new book. It also held a letter from Miss Forman. Grandpa took the letter and read it. Nadine knew more or less what the letter said and she sat waiting to see Grandpa's reaction.

'Hmm,' he said in a serious voice. 'It says here that you had a fight at playtime. Is that true?'

'Yes,' answered Nadine.

'Why?' asked Grandpa, although he had a good idea what might have happened.

'Jodie took my crisps at snack time,' she replied defiantly.

'What? All of them?' asked Grandpa.

'No,' said Nadine.

'Well, how many?'

Nadine hesitated before answering, 'One.'

'Let me see if I've got this right. You had a fight over *one* crisp?' Put like that, Nadine could see why she wasn't going to get any sympathy from Grandpa, but then his voice softened.

'Don't you see what's happening?' he said, 'Everything at home has changed. The new baby takes up Mummy's time. He leaves all his things lying about, and we expect you to want to help to tidy them up. People pop in and out all day to see Mummy and go all gooey over Samuel. Things aren't as they were any more. You get cross then as soon as something upsets you, like Jodie pinching a crisp, snap . . . you lose your temper. Am I right?'

Nadine nodded. 'How do you know Grandpa?'

'Because the same thing happens to grown-ups too,' he replied as he cuddled her closer.

'How do you stop it, Grandpa?'

'Well, I've found that the best thing to do is talk about it. That helps you to understand why you feel angry and that often stops you exploding.' Nadine thought for a while.

'Can I always talk to you about it, Grandpa?'

'That would make me very happy,' he said. They hugged each other. Suddenly the door burst open and the tornado rushed in.

'Hello. I've just seen Samuel. Isn't he just a darling? Our Linda is so lucky having a little boy, isn't she? And she looks so well already, doesn't she?'

Grandpa hardly had time to answer before she went on, 'I told Linda I'll be back tomorrow after work – just to see Samuel's all right. So I'll be off now. Love to both . . . see you. Bye.' and the tornado swept out of the room without waiting for any 'goodbyes'. Grandpa and Nadine were left alone again.

'It won't be easy, Grandpa.'

'No, Mugwump, I'm afraid it won't be easy ... At least, not to begin with.'

Happy Anniversary!

LONG-TERM ABSENCE

It was exactly a year to the day since Shamilla had had her accident. She couldn't remember an awful lot about it, thank goodness, nor the time that she had spent in hospital, but she certainly remembered the three months she had had to spend at home. A lot of that time she had been in bed. She thought about the raw patches on her elbows and ankles, worn sore from rubbing on the sheets as she tried to ease herself into more comfortable positions. She remembered trying to manoeuvre the huge plaster cast that had extended from the top of her hip right down to her little toe. It was needed to ensure that the pins holding her hip bone in position didn't move before the bones fused together.

Shamilla stood her crutches near the door and carefully sat down on the bed. She reached into her bedside table drawer and brought out a scrapbook. She opened the cover. She often felt herself drawn to the scrapbook to look at it over and over again, and today she was going to read it because it was a special anniversary day. It was full of letters and photographs she had exchanged with her friend throughout those months. They reassured her and somehow put all the things that happened over the past year into some sort of order. They had been so important, a chain of letters and images that had joined her to the outside world, when she felt isolated and tired of being alone. She was pleased that Sita had kept her letters too, and had offered them to her to make her scrapbook complete.

First she turned over the page that held the newspaper cutting about the accident, and then she read the first of the letters.

Bradwell School,
Tuesday 26th September

Dear Shamilla,

Miss Forman told us that you came out of hospital yesterday, and I hope you are feeling better. We decided to send you letters to let you know what is happening in school this week. Everything is just about the same as usual except that there is a student who is going to be in our class for about three weeks. I think he is dishy, but he doesn't say very much.

Joe and Simon got into trouble last week because they were fighting in the playground. Lynzi is my best friend now and we share our snack and she lets me sit next to her at lunch. She is also helping me with my sums and I have taught her how to do up her shoe laces. She said that she always had buckles before and so she never learnt when she was little.

Jamail did a great picture of a rocket and it is on the wall now. We are still finding out about space and everything. I am trying to make a pastel picture of Mars, but my sleeves keep dragging across it and my mum gets cross when she sees my red and orange sleeves. Do you believe in Martians? I don't think I do, but I believe in UFOs.

Write and tell me how you are feeling if you can.

Lots of love,

Sita.

P.S. I am sending you a picture of a UFO. I made it up. I think it is called a hoax.

26 Mayfield Gardens
30th September

Dear Sita,

Thank you for your letter and your picture of a UFO. What planet did it come from? Did you take a photo of the aliens?

I am starting to feel a bit better now, but I am fed up with being in bed. The plaster on my leg is very heavy and I keep banging my good knee on it when I turn over. It stops me sitting up properly and so I have to lean over on my side to write this letter. Sorry about the writing.

I had a visitor yesterday, Mrs Partridge, who is going to teach me at home each afternoon, so that I can keep my reading and sums up with you lot. She seems quite nice and I don't think that she will make me work too hard. She is going to start this afternoon. I'll let you know what she is like. I've also had a visit from a physiotherapist lady who gave me lots of exercises to do with my toes and my left hand. I was very tired afterwards, and I had to have a sleep. She says I have to practice every day. I don't want to, but Dad says that I have to.

I miss not being at school already. I never thought that I would miss doing P.E., but I do.

Write as soon as you can.

Love,

Shamilla.

Bradwell School
4th October

Dear Shamilla,

I was surprised to hear about your special teacher. Are you going to do the same sums as we are doing?

We are doing Fractions. I think they are easy. There is lots of colouring in to do.

I've finished my Mars and cut it out. It is on the wall display and all the other planets are up there too. It looks fantastic. I think it is the best frieze we have done yet. We all have to make a moon buggy or a rocket next, but I would rather make an Alien to go with my UFO picture. I think it will be greyish purple with five big eyes. I am sending you a picture of it so that you will recognise it if you see it.

There isn't a lot of news because of the weekend. I didn't see Lynzi this weekend because she had to go shopping for a new schoolbag. She got a pinky-blue one with seven zips on it. It's great.

Everyone is going to write a bit of news for you and send it at the end of the week. It will look a bit like a newspaper. Jamail is going to be the Editor and he gets to decide what goes in it. He wouldn't let Ben put in a bit about his neighbour's dog being run over because he thought you would get upset reading about another accident.

It's my Mum's birthday next week. Have you any idea what I can get her?

Write back soon,

love,

Sita.

26 Mayfield Gardens
Sunday 8th October

Dear Sita,

There was no Physio today and no Mrs Partridge. She is very nice, but she leaves me work to do and I feel bad if I don't do it.

I wasn't feeling very well last week and the doctor gave me some antibiotics again. They made me feel sleepy. I'm fed up being in bed all day and I wish I was back at school again. Mrs Partridge had a good idea. She is going to bring her tape recorder in next Tuesday and we are going to send a message to Miss Forman and everybody. Do you think anyone will send a message back?

I really liked the newsletter. I got it on Friday. Who did the little drawings? They were great. Please say thank you to Philip for sending me a photo of his new little rabbit. Tell him that I think Buffy is a good name for her.

Have you finished fractions yet? I am still working on page 18. I will try to finish them before Tuesday so that I can have more time to work on the tapes.

I'll have to go now because I am getting very tired again. Can't think of what you can get your Mum. What about chocolates?

Thanks for your letters, write soon,

love,

Shamilla.

Bradwell School
14th October

Dear Shamilla,

Surprise! Here is a video for you to see. Mr Peters lent us the camcorder for a while, so that we could all send you a message. We are practising our new hymn for assembly, and Ben looks as if he is picking his nose on the video. I am standing next to Lynzi. We are wearing matching hair bobbles.

You can see our 'Planets' display. Didn't I tell you it was good? And what do you think about our student? He still doesn't say very much. He did most of the videoing and I think he did a good job. You can also see that David's front tooth came out – at last. He was wiggling it for days. He said that he swallowed it, but I don't believe him. I think that he said that to make Lynzi and I feel sick.

How is your leg doing? Do you still get the Physiotherapist lady coming to see you? I think she must be an Alien in disguise. Look behind her neck and if it looks greyish purple, then she is an Alien wearing a wig. Look for her other three eyes, but be careful you don't get caught. She could transport you back to the UFO for experiments.

Take care.

Love from your friend,

Sita.

26 Mayfield Gardens
19th October

Dear Sita,

I have watched the video a few times. I don't think Ben was really picking his nose, I think he was just scratching it. I see what you mean about the 'Planets'. It's the best display we've ever made. The models of rockets look real against that background. You should do a space video with them ... Star Wars 5 or something. I keep laughing at Simon. He keeps popping his head into the picture then popping out again. He must have followed the camera around all day.

I have good news for you. I get part of my plaster off next week and if that goes well then I might be able to get into a wheelchair. I'm keeping my fingers crossed that I will soon be able to come back to school.

I am sending a photo of my room and my cat Bernard. He spends a lot of time on the end of my bed. He is very friendly and cheers me up. I am also going to write to Miss Forman to thank her for the video. It was a great idea. I wish I had a camcorder, then I could show you all my plaster and my room. Do you think Mrs Partridge will be able to borrow one? I shall see her tomorrow.

Bye for now,

Lots of love,

Shamilla.

P.S. I think you are right about the Physiotherapist lady, because her neck looked greyish. I have a feeling she is experimenting on my leg and sending important information back to her planet. If I complain too much she might suspect that I know who she is. I haven't found her other eyes yet. I'll keep looking.

Bye again,

Shamilla.

It wasn't necessary to read every letter or look at every photo. Each time she found she read fewer and fewer lines.

She glanced across at her crutches and pulled a face.

'You needn't look so smug,' she said to them, 'The Alien said I can get rid of you any time now and walk by myself!'

She smiled when she thought of her Physiotherapist. Aliens could be really nice.

'But I never did find her other three eyes!'

Who Cares?

CHILDREN AS CARERS

Elizabeth slowly went down the last two steps of the school bus that had pulled up just at her road end. She helped young Samuel down as the steps were too steep for him. The bus doors pneumatically closed behind them, muffling the shouting, laughing children who were staying on the bus.

Young Samuel ran down the track to the cottage swinging his schoolbag round, and making sure he went through every puddle and muddy patch on the way.

'Keep out of the mud, Our Samuel, or I'll tell Mum,' but Elizabeth knew he couldn't hear because he was too far away. He got to the kitchen door first and dropped his bag by the cooker and ran into the living-room. By the time Elizabeth got to the door it was too late to get him to take off his shoes and the trail of mud went from the kitchen, through the hall and into the living-room. Elizabeth followed it, and came to a halt in front of the settee. The fire had gone out. The room was cold so she knew that the fire had been out for some time. She collected a handful of sticks from the log-box and laid them carefully across the embers that showed any kind of life.

A blanket-covered huddled figure on the settee began to move slowly.

'Hello Flower,' said her mum. 'I must have dozed off again. Is it that time already? I don't know where the time goes. Here, I'll give you a hand with that . . . '

'No, it's OK Mum. I can do it. Samuel, put the kettle on,' said Elizabeth sternly. Samuel moaned,

'Oh, Lizzy . . . '

'Just do it Samuel!' Her voice was insistent and she turned again to the fire, adding coal from the scuttle where she thought it would catch light easily.

Samuel didn't come back into the living-room. He stayed in the kitchen arranging cups and saucers on a tray, and Elizabeth went into the kitchen to wash her hands.

'There's no need for a tray yet, she's asleep again. We'll just have toast or something shall we?'

'Can I have a jacket potato and some cheese please?' asked Samuel.

'Yes, me too I think. You get the cheese and I'll wash the potatoes.'

The two children worked along-side each other in the cramped cottage kitchen that was icy cold. Elizabeth made two Cuppa-soups to warm them up and they sat at the table waiting for the microwave to ting. They warmed their hands on the mugs.

'What did you do at school today, Samuel?'

'I painted a picture of a fish. Do you want to see it?'

He dragged a crumpled painting out of his bag and straightened it out on the table carefully explaining that she shouldn't be shocked by the strange mixture of colours because it was a magical fish that lived far beneath the sea in a sub-marine land . . . But he was suddenly interrupted by a quiet call from the living-room, which coincided with the ting from the microwave.

'You do the potatoes, I'll go in,' stated Elizabeth.

In the room her mother was awake, but still in that sleepy slowed-down state that she seemed to spend most of her day in. Elizabeth held her hand as she gradually became more understandable.

'Have you had something for tea? Are you both warm enough? Is Samuel OK?'

'Yes, we're both fine Mum. Do you want something to eat now?' asked Elizabeth tenderly.

'Yes, I think I can manage a little something. What have we got?'

'I've made you a jacket potato with cheese.'

'No, not cheese, Love. Is there any tuna? I just fancy tuna.'

'I'll see. I'll be back in a minute. Don't go back to sleep yet will you?'

'OK Love,' complied her mother.

Elizabeth went back into the kitchen and opened a tin of tuna and mixed it in a dish with a little salad-cream. Then she lifted her hot jacket potato and scraped all the cheese out of it. Samuel stared at her with a questioning look on his face.

'You said you wanted cheese, didn't you?'

'It's OK Samuel, it's not for me. I'll give this one to Mum. I'll have mine later.' Wearily she lifted a knife and fork and put the meal on the tray. 'Better make the tea now.'

Walking back into the living-room Elizabeth gave a sigh. She could see from the way her mother was slumped into the pillows that she was already dozing, if not fully asleep. Elizabeth pleaded,

'Wake up Mum, here's your tea.'

'Not now darling,' came the slurred words. Elizabeth held back the tears as she took the tray back to the kitchen.

'No luck then?' asked Samuel, and after looking at Elizabeth's eyes he too sighed and his whole body seemed to slump deeper into the chair. Elizabeth let the tray land on the table with a clatter, but she wouldn't let the tears fall.

After she had eaten her jacket potato she helped Samuel with his reading homework. She washed up. She put new bed-clothes on her parent's bed and put the dirty ones in the washing-machine and filled the plastic tray with powder, selected the right programme and set the dial. She made sure the fire didn't go out again. She made her mother a sandwich at about eight o'clock and was pleased to see it half eaten before her mother took another tablet and began to doze again. Then she cleared the mud off the carpets.

At nine, she sent Samuel to bed and took the coal-scuttle to the back door. This, of all the things she had to do, was the worst. Even with an outside light, the track to the coal-shed was dark. It was a relief to see her cat, Melody, sitting on the window-sill. She would have some company outside. The night was bitterly cold but, even so, she opened the door and went out.

The wind blew sharply and wildly. It rustled the trees up in the wood and sent leaves scurrying round the yard. The coal-shed door creaked and groaned as the wind lifted a loose slice of wood up and down. Melody rubbed herself on Elizabeth's legs and the tiny bell on her collar tinkled.

The shovel was heavy with glistening chunks of coal, and Elizabeth shivered as she filled the scuttle. The icy wind stabbed at her cheeks as she leaned against the door to close it. Melody was still there. Rub, rub, tinkle, tinkle.

'Come on, Mel then,' said Elizabeth to the cat, and she lifted the scuttle with two hands. With a rolling, heaving kind of walk she staggered back to the kitchen. Inside felt warmer than before.

By about ten o'clock Elizabeth had fed the cat, made another jacket potato, ironed three shirts and a pair of Samuel's trousers, and done her homework. She sat at the fire-side looking at her mother's thin hands on the blanket. She looked at the grey paper-thin skin that had a yellow appearance in the light of the fire. She let her eyes drift across the collection of tablets on the table beside her mother's head. Bottles and packets! Foil wrappings and plastic bubbles! How she hated seeing them all.

At half past ten her dad came in. He was cold and looked tired.

'Hi, Love. How's things?' he asked.

'OK.' She said what he wanted to hear. 'Mum's asleep but she's had some sandwich and a cup of tea.'

'Have you and Samuel eaten?' asked her father as he washed his hands at the kitchen sink.

'Yes, no problem. I've left you a couple of potatoes and there's cheese and tuna. Do you want soup as well?'

'No thanks. This'll do fine. Is Samuel in bed?'

'Yes, he went about nine. I'm just going to make a hot-water bottle and go.' said Elizabeth, hoping that he wouldn't ask too many questions as she was so tired she couldn't keep her eyes open.

'You go to bed Love and I'll bring your bottle in when it's ready.'

Thankfully, Elizabeth left the kitchen and went to the bedroom which she shared with Samuel. She could tell from his breathing that he was deeply asleep. She changed into her warmest pyjamas and snuggled into her own bed and nestled under the covers, keeping her mouth under them so that her warm breath would heat them up quicker.

She didn't see her father slip the hot-water bottle next to her feet. She was already asleep.

The next day at about two o'clock the warmth of the classroom enveloped Elizabeth like a comfortable electric blanket. The voices of the other children grew fuzzy and faint and she drifted contentedly into a wonderful dreamless sleep.

Miss Forman looked at her relaxed body across the desk and she decided that it was time to ask Elizabeth's parents to come to the school. There was something very wrong if a child fell asleep at her desk three times in one week. She considered the possibilities. It could be that Elizabeth was sickening for something, but it could also be that she was being allowed to stay up too late, or maybe she wasn't sleeping well for some reason. Miss Forman took one of the typewritten letters that she kept in the drawer and filled in Elizabeth's name. It was a letter asking her parents to make an appointment as soon as possible. When Elizabeth woke up she would give her the letter, but for now it was best to let her sleep.

At the end of the day Elizabeth began to wake as the final bell rang. She presumed that since Miss Forman hadn't asked to speak to her, that her quick sleep had gone unnoticed and she had no idea how long she had been sleeping or if she had merely been daydreaming. She was almost out of the door when her teacher caught up with her and handed her the sealed envelope.

'Could you give this to your mum or dad Elizabeth? Put it in your schoolbag so you don't leave it on the bus.' And since Elizabeth had no idea what the letter was about she unzipped her bag and put the letter inside her reading book.

At home again, Elizabeth put the letter on the mantelpiece and went through her evening routine. They had beans on toast. There was more washing for the machine. The coal-scuttle got filled. Samuel did his reading. Her mum managed to keep down some tomato soup, but couldn't eat the sandwiches. Dad got home from the lorry depot at about half past ten. She forgot about the letter and curled up in bed, exhausted.

She did this for one more day and then it was the weekend. Dad got a day off and she and Samuel had a chance to play in the garden. They went shopping with Dad and then they waited in the kitchen when the doctor called. As usual they could hear raised voices. The doctor was saying something about going into care, whatever that was, and again Dad was saying 'over my dead body' and 'we can manage.' Then the doctor talked about hospital and Dad said that it wasn't necessary.

On Monday Elizabeth's day began as usual. She dressed Samuel while her dad helped her mum to get dressed. Between them they managed to light the fire, set out a hot flask and some biscuits on a tray, wash up and hang out a load of washing. This was all before the school bus arrived. It was a special day off for her dad and so she was more happy than usual because she knew she would not have the meals to make or any of the housework to do. Perhaps he would have time to make a proper meal – maybe mince and potatoes or a real vegetable soup. She smiled to herself when she thought of an evening without the coal scuttle to fill.

At the end of the day a message came from the office. The secretary came to the classroom to say that Elizabeth and Samuel were to stay in the playground until their daddy came to collect them.

Elizabeth's mind was confused and frightened. What could have happened to bring her dad to the school?

She played with Samuel in the last of the afternoon's wintry sunshine until the secretary came out into the playground to collect them both and she led them back to the office while she chatted about the weekend. In the office her dad was sitting in one of the armchairs with a cup of tea perched awkwardly on his knees.

'Hello kids,' he greeted them. 'Come on in.'

Mr Peters held the door open for them as they came warily into the room, but as their dad noticed the anxious look in their eyes he quickly added,

'It's all right. It's not Mum.'

'Your Dad was just explaining about your mum not being well. You've got a lot of work to do at home haven't you, Elizabeth? We were trying to work out some way of making things easier for you if we can,' went on Mr Peters. 'One idea is to get you some help with your homework, and Samuel's too. One of the other mothers pops in each day to hear some of the infants reading. If you like she can help you and Samuel with your reading and any other homework as well. What do you think?'

That would help, thought Elizabeth. Samuel could be quite stubborn about his reading if he felt like it. That would be one less job to do at night. Her dad interrupted her train of thought by adding,

'And Mr Peters is quite worried because you fall asleep in the afternoon.'

'I don't mean to,' began Elizabeth.

'It's all right. I'm not cross and nor is Mr Peters. I'm sorry because I didn't realise you were doing so much at home.'

Elizabeth didn't answer. She wanted to be able to say that it didn't matter and that she didn't mind being tired, but she was so worn out that she didn't argue.

'So, Love. I've decided to get some help in the house – a home-help. I know we didn't want one, but we'll just have to get used to the idea because we can't go on like this. We want Mum to stay at home for as long as she can, but now we need a bit of help. What about it Love?'

Elizabeth smiled and then flung her arms around her dad's neck and clung closely to him. She loved her dad and she knew that he hated outsiders coming into his home and 'busy-bodying'. She stayed like this for a few minutes before saying,

'It'll be fine Dad. Shall we go home?'

'Yes Love. Let's go home.'

I Want To Be Like You

BODY IMAGE AND EATING DISORDERS

After making sure that the door was locked, Jodie sat down on the lid of the toilet and didn't try to hold back the tears. She looked down at the tops of her legs as they were splayed out across the lid. She studied the tiny flower print of her skirt. In the magazine it had looked so sophisticated – so grown up, but now she could scarcely make out the pattern through her tears.

Music changed to a quicker, livelier dance in the hall. It was funny, but whatever the teachers did to the Hall – decorations, a frieze, new spotlights – it always still looked like the Hall. It couldn't be disguised enough, and at the thought of the word disguise she began to feel desolate again. And she was hungry. She had made her usual excuse about breakfast, and nobody had noticed because they were all so busy getting ready themselves. Lunch hadn't been so easy to avoid now that there were two dinner ladies, but pretending to have an upset stomach had been a brain wave.

Then she had managed to convince Mum that she had already eaten something at Sarita's house to please Sarita's mother, and that was why she wasn't really hungry enough for tea. She promised to eat something after the disco, just to please Mum.

Suddenly the outer door burst open and clanged against the doorstop. Girls were laughing. How many were there, two or three? Jodie lifted her feet off the ground and kept very still. She didn't want to be seen or heard.

'You go first then.'

'OK.'

'What do you think of Mister Brown?'

More giggling.

'You mean *Max*.' Even more giggling. 'I love his waistcoat. It makes him look even taller.'

The toilet flushed and a third voice said,

'Well, I think he fancies himself and is just showing off to the other teachers. I think he is *sad*.' And with that someone opened the outer door again and the troop of girls left the toilet and wandered down the corridor leaving the door to clang shut behind them.

Jodie thought about the magazine that she had bought at the weekend, and now wished she hadn't. It was there that she had seen the skirt and it had looked fabulous. The model had a similar hairstyle, shoulder-length, blonde, and swept back from her face a little. Jodie wondered if *she* had to use handfuls of mousse and cans of spray to keep *her* hair in position all day. Some days it was a real struggle to keep that fringe just in the right place, especially if it was raining or windy.

The model had a close-fitting blouse that met the skirt at the waistband, and of course the model had long, long legs. At the thought of those long legs the tears welled up again. Jodie could hear the music beating its way from the Hall. She longed to join in the dancing and the fun, but she couldn't go back in there.

Suddenly the outer door sprung open and lots of voices echoed around the large block of toilets, and again Jodie raised her legs and kept as still as she could until she heard the group of girls leave. They sounded as if they were having so much fun out there, and she felt such an outsider.

'Jodie?' It was Sarita's voice. 'Jodie, I know you are in there.'

But she couldn't answer.

'Jodie open up will you? What's the matter? Why did you run off like that? I've looked everywhere for you. Are you all right?'

The genuine concern in Sarita's voice made Jodie more upset. She desperately wanted to hold on to her friend, to cry and be able to tell her why she was crying and hiding. Jodie began to sob and Sarita could now hear her and she became alarmed.

'What's the matter? Are you sick? Shall I get one of the teachers for you? Please Jodie. Please tell me.'

Hesitantly Jodie opened the cubicle door and simply said, 'Look!'

At first Sarita didn't know what she was supposed to be looking at, until she noticed the skirt which exactly matched her own.

'So what?' she said in bewilderment.

Sensing that her friend was having difficulty in understanding, Jodie continued,

'It looks great on you Sarita, but it just makes me look fatter,' and she put her hand up to her mouth to stifle her sobs.

'No it doesn't,' protested Sarita. 'How can it make you look fatter when you are not fat in the first place?'

'I am, I am. Look at these thighs!' She roughly struck her own thighs to demonstrate. 'They wobble!' snapped Jodie.

'They are supposed to!' Sarita snapped back.

Jodie looked up defiantly.

'Yours don't!'

'No, but do you know what my brothers call me?' asked Sarita, who then answered her own question. 'Sticky the stick insect!'

Jodie couldn't help but laugh, but Sarita would not be stopped.

'They go on about it all the time. It makes me mad. Ragid says that my name should have been "Lucky".'

'Lucky?' asked Jodie.

'Yes, Lucky-your-legs-don't-snap!'

Both girls burst out laughing, and could only talk again when the laughing had subsided.

'Jodie, I saw this in Craze magazine and went out and bought it but it looks stupid on me. I should never have asked Mum to buy it for me. It just makes my legs look even thinner. I don't know why I didn't realise that in the shop. And it's so short that it rides up at the back and I don't dare to bend over at all.'

Jodie smiled ready to confide too.

'Mine makes my legs look fat. Black tights might have helped, but even so I still think they would have looked short and fat. But the picture was so good, wasn't it? *Her* legs didn't look short or fat!'

'But supermodels don't have to move around. They just pose in the best positions and click, click, click.' Sarita imitated a photographer. 'Did you know that if the picture isn't just perfect, they trim bits off before they print it.'

'I wish I could trim bits off.' Jodie was still not convinced.

'Jodie, nobody looks like models except . . . well . . . models. You are *not* fat.'

'Well, you are not skinny either. I wish I had legs like yours.'

'And I wish my legs were more like yours.'

The girls smiled at each other.

'I think it's a stupid skirt and it doesn't suit either of us,' stated Jodie.

'I agree.'

Just at that moment, Miss Forman put her head round the door.

'Is everything all right in here girls?'

'Yes Miss,' they replied.

'Fine.' Miss Forman turned to go, but something caught her eye and she commented, 'and by the way, I love the skirts.'

Both of the girls stared in amazement and then burst into laughter, which Miss Forman could still hear as she made her way back to the Hall and the disco.

'Silly girls,' she remarked as she shook her head.

Mad Bob

UNDERSTANDING DISABILITY

There was hardly any noise at Bob's end of the street. The orange glow of the street-light faded out before it reached his front door, and there were only two lamp-posts down his end of the scheme anyway.

Then out of the darkness came the familiar voices, the laughter, and the clatter of the empty ring-pull can rattling along the road. Bob knew who was kicking that can. He knew what would happen next. He didn't move, but held his torch tighter and shivered a little as the wind cut into his neck.

'Come on out, Mad Bob!' That was the first of the taunts, followed immediately by laughter. 'Come and see what we've got for you tonight!' But Bob didn't move away from his hiding place in the alley. 'We've brung stones and we've brung bricks for you tonight!' More laughter.

Bob tried to see how many boys there were this time. He could make out two tall youths that he thought were about fourteen or fifteen. There were at least three younger boys standing a little way behind them. He couldn't make out what they were saying.

'Leave him alone Dougie. Let's go back to the swing park.'

'Naw. He's just had his windows re-done. We'll have a bit of fun first.'

'It's not worth it, Dougie. Leave him be.'

'Naw. I've fetched some bits and pieces. I want to do a little experiment to see which works the best, bricks or stones!'

The other big boy burst out laughing and some of the youngsters copied by giggling raucously.

'Bet you a fiver the bricks win.'

'You haven't got a fiver!'

'So what?'

The two older boys fell about laughing and Dougie sat down on somebody's low garden wall.

'Anyway, you haven't got any bricks!' challenged one of the young boys.

In response, Dougie jumped up and kicked the fancy edging bricks off the wall he had been sitting on and picked one of them up.

'I have now,' he said as he raised his arm to throw it. One of the young boys became alarmed.

'Don't Dougie,' he said before he remembered that *nobody* told Dougie what to do. Dougie froze just as he was about to let go of the brick.

'Don't Dougie!' he mocked the smaller boy's voice. 'Mummy wouldn't like it, Dougie. Don't be a bad boy Dougie!' he continued. 'What's the matter Mickey? Are you scared? Scared in case big bad Mad Bob comes out to chase us again? Scared in case he shouts at you with his stupid voice? Dougie's voice changed as he tried to mock Bob's slow, deep drawl. 'Don't do that you boys!'

Dougie moved closer to Mickey's face until their breaths mingled. Mickey tried to move back because of the strong smell of lager, but Dougie's hand sprung out and grasped his shoulder. Mickey could feel the pressure of the grip and he was afraid.

'Course I'm not – don't be daft.' Mickey tried to sound convincing.

'Then *you* do it!' Dougie screamed.

'Do what?'

'*You* chuck the brick! *You* put out the new windows,' and he lifted Mickey's hand and roughly twisted the brick into it, forcing his fingers around it. He looked menacingly into Mickey's eyes. 'Go on Mickey, *you* do it!'

Mickey didn't want to. He wasn't afraid of Mad Bob. In fact he didn't like him nor dislike him. He didn't know him. He'd only seen him lumbering down the High Street in his old overcoat that nearly touched his shoes, and his muddy coloured flat-cap that he pulled down over his thick-lensed glasses. He knew that the other boys didn't like Mad Bob because he shouted at them and threatened to chase them. But Mickey thought that he only did that because the boys shouted in his letter box whenever it got dark and they called him names when he went down the street. Once Dougie had ambushed him and pelted him with rotten apples. He had managed to hit him on the head and knock his cap off, and all the boys had howled with laughter as he groped on the ground trying to find it. When he eventually got it, he had given them a good chase, but he could never catch them because he was far too slow and stumbling. He had shouted that he would tell the police. Then Dougie had decided that this was now war and that is how the stone throwing had begun. Every weekend for the last three weeks they had gone around to his house and shouted taunts, and then Dougie would always throw stones until he broke a window.

Mickey looked up into Dougie's eyes. He was afraid of those eyes.

'Go on. What's stopping you?'

'Nothing.'

'Go on then!'

Mickey took the brick and walked towards Mad Bob's garden wall. He managed to throw it, but it fell short and landed with a soft thud in the damp earth of the flower garden. The bigger boys jeered and laughed.

'You're useless, Wimp! Have another go.'

Dougie kicked another brick loose from the wall and handed it to Mickey.

'Go nearer you idiot!' Dougie sneered and so Mickey nervously went through the garden gate and along the path to the window.

Suddenly out of the black depths of the alley-way shone a blinding beam of light, and there was yelling and panic behind him.

'It's him. Run for it!'

'Get out of the way. Move it!'

'Got you!'

Mickey screamed. He was blinded by the torchlight, and couldn't see Bob's hand as it grabbed the hood of his jacket and almost swung him round.

'Get off! Let me go!' Mickey protested.

'No!' yelled Mad Bob.

Mickey's jacket was zipped right up to his neck and there was no way he could wriggle out of it. He was being hauled along the path and through the doorway into a dimly lit hall. The front door slammed shut. He was now alone with Mad Bob.

'Don't hurt me! Don't hurt me!' pleaded Mickey.

Mad Bob's voice was deep and slow and breathy.

'No,' he said. He raised his hand to Mickey's face. Mickey squirmed, expecting a blow but, instead, the hand slowly raised his chin, so that their eyes met. Behind his thick glasses Mad Bob's eyes seemed to be calm in the misty half-light of the hall.

'I – won't – hurt – you,' Bob mouthed slowly and precisely.

'Yes you will. You're mad. Everyone says so. I want to go home. Don't you hurt me or my dad will get you!' The words spilled out. Then Mickey suddenly realised that Mad Bob was carefully studying his lips as he spoke.

'I – won't – hurt – you,' Bob mouthed slowly and carefully again.

There was something about the way he looked at his face, about the slow way that he spoke, about his funny voice. Then Mickey realised what it was. Mad Bob was deaf. He suddenly felt so ashamed of what he had tried to do to a handicapped man. He lowered his face to look at the ground.

'I didn't know, I didn't realise . . . ' he stammered.

Bob slowly, but firmly, lifted Mickey's chin again.

'Look – at – me,' he insisted.

'I'm sorry.' Mickey said loudly and slowly.

'You must look at me when you speak. I read your lips.'

'I didn't know.'

'You didn't care.' Holding on to Mickey's arm, Bob walked him through the living-room doorway into a sparsely furnished room, heated by a small electric fire.

'Sit down.'

Mickey did as he was told. He looked around him and saw there were a few photos on the mantelpiece and a couple of squashy looking armchairs. He chose the one nearest to the door. Bob sat on the other. He looked at Mickey.

'Do you want a cup of tea?'

Mickey was so surprised at this offer that he blurted out, 'Yes.'

'I'll show you the kitchen.' Bob got up and led Mickey into the kitchen where he plugged in the kettle. He moved quite slowly and seemed to feel for things, like the socket, the tap – feeling his way along the worktop to the tea-caddy.

'Milk? Sugar?' simple questions.

'Yes please.'

'What? Look at me.'

Mickey looked up. 'Yes please.'

'Better.'

Mickey watched Bob silently as he made two mugs of tea. He put them on a tray, and Mickey knew that they were going back to the living-room. This meant going into the hall again, and although he could see the front door clearly, it didn't seem necessary any more to make a run for it. Mad Bob wasn't mad and he wasn't bad. He was deaf. Mickey was interested in this man who had caught him trying to smash his windows with a brick and, instead of hitting him, had made him a cup of tea. They sat down again on the squashy armchairs, and Mickey studied the bits and pieces around the room. The rug was worn thin, and an old cupboard had a handle missing. It was so quiet. There wasn't a television. There wasn't a clock. He touched Bob's arm to draw his attention.

'You haven't got a clock,' he sounded slowly.

'No point. I can't see the hands very well. I've got a watch.' He held out his arm to show a wrist watch with no face. He flicked a button on the side and the case sprung up to show a clock made out of little dots.

'Got bad eyes too. I have to feel the time.'

'Can't you see much?' asked Mickey, 'You can see me, can't you?'

'Worse at night,' answered Bob.

Mickey nodded to show that he understood. They sat for a while longer enjoying the hot tea. Then Mickey touched Bob's arm again. Bob turned towards him.

'Have you always been deaf?'

'Yes. Born just about totally deaf. I can only hear very loud things. I can hear traffic, big lorries, jet planes. But I was ill when I was ten and I lost my good eyesight. Now I need thick glasses, and I still don't see very well.'

'So you won't need a telly?'

'No. No telly, and no radio, but I do have Silky.'

'Silky?' inquired Mickey.

'My little cat.'

'Can I see her?' Mickey liked cats. He had one of his own, a big ginger tomcat called Buster.

'Silky is out. I put her out after tea in case she got hurt by the glass.'

Mickey felt an icy shiver of shame trickle down his spine. He couldn't explain how sorry he was for what he and the others had done, so he just sat there with his head bowed in silence. Eventually, he looked up and saw Bob looking at him.

'I . . . I won't throw bricks at you again.' Tears welled into his eyes. 'Promise . . . but I can't stop Dougie.'

'Don't be his friend. Don't watch. Don't join in.' Bob's voice was firm and strong.

They sat quietly together again.

'Can I come back and see Silky?'

Bob smiled. 'Friends are always welcome. Friends always get tea.'

Mickey smiled back. He walked to the front door and Bob opened it for him.

As he walked outside, Mickey had half expected to see Dougie and the gang by the doorstep jumping out of the darkness to rescue him, but they had gone. None of them had helped him or even stayed to see if he had got out alive. They had all run away scared. Scared of a lonely deaf man who was nearly blind. Mad Bob. Then he realised the awful truth. It wasn't Bob who was mad, it was Dougie.

He walked through the housing scheme trying to get home quickly. He turned the corner and found himself almost tripping over Dougie's legs. All the boys were sitting on the ground, out of sight of Mad Bob's house and there was a paper bag in Dougie's hands.

'Oh. There you are. We wondered where you'd got to. Here, we've got some unfinished business with Mad Bob.' He thrust an unlit firework into Mickey's hand.

Going Home

TEMPORARY ACCOMMODATION

The sun was shining hazily through a thick mist which seemed to have collected at the far end of the playground. It was a damp and foggy October morning. Children huddled in groups, talking loudly about last night's television and videos. Everything seemed quite settled as friends met friends at the beginning of the day.

A small dark figure clung to the edge of the mist and kept its distance from all the groups. The mist muffled shrieks and yells from the football fields, but it couldn't disguise the piercing ring of the bell. Hesitantly, clusters of pupils walked to the doors and arranged themselves into lines. The dark figure grew clearer, and Thomas approached his own line, tagging onto the end. The stiff metal doors crashed open and two nodding teachers stepped out onto the tarmac. The noise from the lines began to quieten, until there was only the occasional shuffle and cough.

'Hold the door please Elizabeth. Take your line in Gareth. Wipe your feet as you go.'

'Not a very good start to the day, is it, Mr Logan? I hope that it clears by breaktime.'

The two teachers continued to talk as all their pupils filed into the school. Once inside, the chattering began to build up again. There was the tumbling over abandoned coats and bags, and the usual hunt for indoor shoes. Chairs clattered as they were taken down from the tables. There were notes to be collected, money for the trip to be recorded, letter slips to be hunted out of schoolbags, dinner money to be sorted out, and tuck shop crisps to be paid for, then order was restored as the class settled in front of the blackboard to hear the first instructions of the day.

'Let me just remind you to bring your trip money in by Friday, if you haven't brought it in to me already. Thomas, don't forget that I need the reply slip for the trip. It's very important. No slip, no trip. We are not allowed to take you if your mum doesn't sign the slip. OK?'

Thomas nodded and said nothing. He didn't want to listen to anything else that morning. Work continued, but just before playtime he got a row from Jodie for not concentrating on his maths. She was his partner, and she felt that he wasn't thinking at all. By playtime, Jodie had had enough. Thomas had ruined two charts she was trying to colour in.

'No, I said blue. Blue! Blue! What are you thinking of?' She removed the pink felt pen from his hand and replaced it with a blue one. 'Blue!'

Thomas's eyes blazed with an anger that he could not control, and suddenly he flung the blue pen as far across the room as he could. Zoe squealed as it clattered against a unit full of trays. Silence fell across the room for a few seconds, and was shattered by the school bell.

'Quietly leave everything just where it is, and tiptoe out to play. Thomas come and see me please.'

Miss Forman waited until everyone was out of the classroom and tangled up in the cloakroom before drawing up a small chair and sitting directly in front of Thomas.

'You haven't been very happy all morning Thomas. I don't think you've been really happy all week, have you?'

Thomas made no reply, but the edge of his ears went pink, while the rest of his face stayed unusually white.

'Are you still living at Broadleas?' This brought a little flicker of a shadow into Thomas' eyes. 'I'm sure you won't have to stay there for long . . . '

'We haven't got a house now,' interrupted Thomas, ' and I don't know where we'll live. Do you know, those people are dirty?'

'Well, I don't suppose there is a washing machine in the home,' suggested Miss Forman.

'No, not mucky. Dirty!'

'What do you mean?' Miss Forman was trying to untangle the trail of Thomas' thoughts.

'They talk dirty. They say bad things. Mum says I'm not to stand near them, but they use the big kitchens when we are there and Mum won't leave me upstairs in our room on my own.'

The story began to make some sense. Miss Forman knew that Thomas' mum and dad had had a big argument and so she had left their home with Thomas. They were now staying in a Council hostel in the town until they could get another place to live. She hadn't realised just what a strain this was for Thomas, who now lived in one huge, cold room at the top of the hostel. Obviously they had to share a kitchen, and by the sound of it there were some nasty people staying there as well.

'Has Mum heard any news about a new house yet?'

'No, and we can't get our things out of our old house until Dad goes. He won't let us in the house.'

'I notice that you don't have your schoolbag,' added Miss Forman, and suddenly realised, 'Is that why you haven't got your reading book?'

Thomas' face began to go red. He had lied to Miss Forman and said he had forgotten his book. He hadn't wanted to tell her where it really was when all of his reading group were listening.

'When you do get your schoolbag out of your old house, bring in the book. I'll lend you another for the time being.'

Thomas was surprised. He'd told a lie, but hadn't got the row he was so afraid of. Instead, Miss Forman seemed to be really concerned and worried for him.

'Look Thomas, this is a hard time for you and your mum. She wants to look after you, but it's hard with only one room, and people around that aren't nice, but it won't be for long. You'll see. The Council will find you somewhere soon. They don't want to see you in Broadleas for very long. Let's see if you get any news by tomorrow.' Thomas' face brightened a little bit. 'There's an old schoolbag in the lost-property cupboard. It's been there for years, so I'm sure the Headteacher will allow me to let you have it until you get your own things back. OK?'

'Yes, then the books won't get wet.'

'Off you go now and have some playtime, before the bell goes, but don't forget to come and talk to me again if anything is upsetting you.'

As Thomas quickly changed his shoes to go outside, he tried to hide the hole in his sock, but Miss Forman had already noticed it.

'You'll get your own clothes back I'm sure. Don't worry.'

Thomas smiled and ran out.

At the end of playtime, Miss Forman gave Thomas the old

schoolbag, a reading book and a new pencil. He felt more like the others now and finished off the morning's work. After lunch-time however, he found that the warmth of the classroom, and the lovely full feeling left by the school dinner in his stomach made it almost impossible to keep his eyes open during storytime. He rested his head on his hands and fell asleep on the desk. Now and again a loud noise burst into his dreamy thoughts, but then he drifted away again into sleep. While he slept, the afternoon lessons finished and his mum came to collect him. Miss Forman didn't want to appear nosy, but she needed to know from Thomas' mum how accurate his story had been, and what was likely to happen next.

'I'm really sorry to hear that you have had to leave your home. Thomas mentioned what has happened. He seems to be very unhappy.'

'I know that I should have told you earlier about Roger and I splitting up, but I've been so upset. I could hardly talk to anyone,' began Mrs Frame.

'How are you finding it, staying at Broadleas? Thomas doesn't like it, from what he's told me,' continued Miss Forman.

'It's an awful place, but Thomas knows that it is only temporary. We've been promised some help from the council, and I've made an appointment to see a solicitor. There must be a way to get our belongings back from our old house. We've only got what I could carry in an old suitcase, and what Thomas could carry in some carrier bags. Roger won't let us back in to get the rest of our things.'

'Surely there must be some way to get your clothes back?' Miss Forman questioned hopefully.

Mrs Frame didn't reply, so Miss Forman changed the subject quickly.

'I let Thomas sleep at the end of the afternoon. He was so tired.'

'We don't get much sleep at Broadleas. There always seems to be a party going on in one of the rooms. Last night one of the women's husbands found out where she was staying and brayed and brayed on the door and there was shouting and screaming. He'd obviously had a lot to drink. We hardly had any sleep, but there's no way I can keep Thomas off school. I have to keep going to work or we'll have no money at all. I'm sorry if he's a bit of a handful at the moment. He doesn't really understand what's going on.'

'That's OK,' smiled Miss Forman, 'we'll keep an eye on him at school, but please let me know how things go on at home. If you can think of any way we can help you at school, just let us know. I've found him a schoolbag. What about gym things – shorts and so on?'

'Have you any spare ones you can lend him?' asked Mrs Frame.

Just then Thomas stretched and yawned and caught sight of his mum.

'Hi-ya Mum. What are you doing here? Is it time to go home yet? Can we get my toys now?'

'Not yet son. Come and get your coat, it's time to go.'

As they left discussing the egg and chips they would be having for tea, Miss Forman thought how close the two of them were. If anyone could get through hard times like these, then Mrs Frame and Thomas probably would. She turned to the walk-in cupboard to hunt for shorts and a t-shirt.

The next day was almost a repeat of the day before. Thomas was niggly and petulant with other children, and yet when his work didn't go right first time, he burst into tears. He got into trouble at playtime too, and in the middle of the afternoon, fell asleep. By the end of the week, Miss Forman was at her wit's end. She only had to look at Thomas in a cross manner and he burst into floods of sobbing, but with anyone else who crossed his path, he was angry and ready to fight.

On the Friday afternoon, Mrs Frame came into the classroom and noticed a definite heartfelt sigh of relief from Miss Forman.

'I know how you feel,' said Mrs Frame, 'Thomas has been awful at home all week. I'm sure he'll have been the same here too.'

'Yes, it's been hard going. It's a good job that it's Friday!' joked Miss Forman.

'Well, next week should be a bit better,' smiled Mrs Frame. 'I've been to the solicitor and he says there's a way to get back our things and move back into our old house. It's Roger who'll have to leave and not us. Thomas is bound to be more settled when we move back – I'll not tell him till it's all organised though, I don't want to get him too excited.'

'When do you think you will be moving back then?' asked Miss Forman.

'Oh, by the end of next week, so the solicitor reckons.'

'I'm so pleased for you.'

'Thank you for your help. I know Thomas has been in a funny mood all week. Thanks for putting up with him.'

'That's all right,' smiled the tired teacher.

On the way home, Miss Forman thought how nice it was that someone had said thank you. It didn't happen all that often, but when it did, it made the whole thing worthwhile. She smiled to herself thinking how pleased Thomas would be when he found out that he would be going home.

Quick! Quick!

JEALOUSY

Clip ran along the edge of the water sniffing for dead seagulls or bits of crabs' legs. He had an awful habit of eating anything he found if it had ever been alive. He rooted out a large stick by nuzzling it and pawing at the sand, eventually loosening it and lifting it in his mouth. He trotted to the path, seaweed trailing like brown ribbons from the end of the stick.

Mhari loved Clip and she took the stick that he offered and disentangled the seaweed. She knew Clip wanted her to throw the stick for him so that he could trot back with it. They usually played this game over and over again until one of them got distracted or too tired to run any more. It was usually Mhari who gave up first.

Her walks went as far as the 'Big House' but hardly ever further than that because the path became rougher and there was a steep drop down to the sea. She was always frightened that Clip would get carried away in one of his sillier moments and charge over the edge of the gully into the water below. The tide had cut deep slashes and trenches into the grassland that was hidden at high tide. It wasn't safe to go further than the Big House on her own.

Mhari had watched the renovation of the Big House for quite a few weeks now. The painter's van had been sitting outside every afternoon for a fortnight. The outside was now sparkling white and the old iron railings shiny deep blue to match the new door. There had been double glazing put in all the windows. The road had been blocked by a large lorry delivering oil for the central heating just last week, and there had been an interior designer's estate car parked outside on quite a few occasions when Mhari had walked by with Clip. So far, however, she had not seen anyone who she thought would live there. She imagined what they would be like.

Well! They'd be incredibly rich for a start. They would have to be, to be able to pay for all the new fittings. Fancy having to pay for a decorator! She always helped her mum to emulsion the walls. Surely these people weren't so helpless that they couldn't use emulsion paint and a roller? Mhari shouted for Clip to come round to the front of the house and she climbed the rocky wall to get a clear view across the garden. That was new! The grass had been cut and some of the hedge trimmed, but there were no workmen there now.

Mhari had imagined the 'Snoot' family, as she called them. Mr Snoot would have a briefcase and drive a large dark green car. He would probably only get to the house at weekends when he finished business in the city. He wouldn't talk nicely to his children and they were so snooty that they didn't care. Mrs Snoot would spend her days picking flowers and arranging them in large vases, and she would shout at the servants – because there would have to be lots of servants. Mrs Snoot would never get her hands dirty. Mhari thought about the 'little Snoots'. They had really expensive mountain bikes which they didn't appreciate and they would throw them onto the gravel and jump on them when they were in a bad temper – which they often were, and then they would kick their yapping snooty dogs. Mhari had never seen the new owners of the Big House, but she knew just what they would be like. Rich and snooty!

Calling Clip to go back down the path with her, Mhari made

her way home. The sun glistened on the wet sand that had been moulded into ripples as the tide had gone out. Far out across the estuary the patches of quicksand shone golden-grey and the oyster-catchers squealed as they trampled and prodded the sand with long beaks searching for food. It was a beautiful view, but Mhari felt unsettled and rather cross. She was still thinking about the Snoots and their luxury house.

Her brother, Sean, ran along the path to meet her. He charged around with Clip as they greeted each other.

'Dad's in,' sang Sean when he was near enough. Mhari's mood brightened straight away.

'Yowee!' she yelled as she ran past Sean up the garden path, followed, and almost tripped up by Clip.

'Hiya!' she called as she flung the dog's lead onto the table. Her eyes searched the room for her dad. Mum was pouring tea in the kitchen.

'He's out the back,' she said, knowing exactly who Mhari was looking for. Mhari went straight through the kitchen and out of the back door, and saw her father bending over the vegetables at the end of the garden. She ran and grabbed him by the neck, almost pulling him over. He clung onto her, laughing.

'Steady on, steady on. You'll have me over lass.'

'I don't care. I don't care.' Mhari laughed back in return and the two of them tumbled forward onto the grass. Clip had caught up with her and was joining in the excitement by licking every bare patch of skin he could find. As the laughter died down she asked,

'When did you get back, Dad?'

A cloud seemed to fall across his face as he answered,

'Just before three. I wasn't due back until Saturday, but five of us got paid off. Not enough work for all of us.' He stared at his hands as if he were ashamed – as if it was his fault that he had lost his job.

'It happens sometimes,' she replied in a grown-up way.

'Aye lass. It happens sometimes.'

They sat for a while looking at the vegetables. She was waiting for him to start the conversation again.

'Well, what's been going on around here while I've been away?' he said in a more lively tone.

'Clip dug up the rhubarb again so Sean replanted it and put a box on top,' she offered.

'Good for him.'

'And there's been a lot of changes at the Big House. It's definitely been sold. The Snoots have had new windows *and* central heating put in.'

'The Snoots?' her dad interrupted, 'Who on earth are the Snoots?'

Mhari looked embarrassed, realising she had told him her nick-name for the new people.

'Oh, they are just the new lot,' she said, lightly. 'I don't know their name yet.'

Her dad laughed and laughed.

'So you call them the Snoots?'

'Well!' she said defensively, 'I reckon they will be, won't they? They've got pots of money. Well, I tell you Dad, they had better not try to tell us what to do!'

He laughed and she laughed and Clip ran round in circles after his tail.

Mum called from the kitchen window, 'Tea's getting cold.'

'Come on lass. Teatime,' said her Dad. They walked together into the kitchen. When Dad tried to close the back door, it wouldn't shut easily, so he had to slam it.

'Aye, I'll have time to fix things around the place now that I'm home.'

Mhari moved a mug nearer to him. She noticed it was chipped, so she quickly swapped it for her unchipped one. Mum put the milk bottle back in the fridge. They sat down to a plate of mince and potatoes and followed that with a slice of homemade gingerbread.

'Any more potatoes Mum?' asked Sean who always lagged behind everyone else at mealtimes.

'Sorry son.' She looked apologetically at her husband. 'I'd have bought more in if I'd known you were coming home.'

But he replied, 'Don't worry about it. That was a treat after what I've been living on these past weeks. I don't care if I never see a fried cafe-breakfast ever again.'

Mum smiled at him.

'Now, what do you say we go for a walk – after we've helped your Mum do the dishes, that is? Then we could come back and watch a bit of telly before we go to bed.'

Mum looked away awkwardly again as she said, 'Sorry Love, but the telly had to go back. We got a bit behind with the rental.'

Everyone waited to see his reaction.

'Ah, who needs a telly anyway! Come on, let's get going.'

They all got up at once and the dishes were in the sink and all over the drainer.

Clip was trying to lick plates in the commotion.

'Oh, leave them be the lot of you,' laughed Mum, 'go and leave me in peace – go on – off you go.'

Dad picked up the dog lead, not needing to be asked twice, and the children ran ahead of him onto the path.

'Take a cardi with you. It'll get cold.' called Mum after them, but it was too late, they were already striding along the shingle path down to the shore-line.

They walked and chattered. Clip ate a dead something-or-other and promptly vomited it up again. It must have been just a bit too old. There were a few other groups of people walking the shoreline path. On such a beautiful evening there were often kids, couples or folk walking their dogs. Clip usually took no notice of other dogs, so Dad let him roam around without his lead. Clip preferred chasing gulls and oyster-catchers, but he never caught them himself. He just enjoyed the dead ones the tide brought in.

Quite a long way ahead of them, lying on the sand was one such seagull, except when Clip ran near to it, it reared its head and made a frantic dash for the open sea. Its broken wing prevented its flight and it half ran, half paddled in the wet sand and only succeeded in going around in circles. Clip thought this was wonderful fun and he ran round and round the gull, barking wildly, not knowing what to do with a live one. He kept shepherding the gull around the sand. It jabbed its beak at his legs making him yelp and bark. The children ran towards him trying to shoo him away from the crippled seagull.

Suddenly Dad yelled, 'Stop Mhari! Sean! Stop!' His voice was so alarming that both children stopped immediately still some distance away from Clip. 'Walk back to me. Just the way you went. Follow your footsteps.'

The children instinctively obeyed him and now that they had slowed down they felt how soft the sand was beneath their feet. They had run into a stretch of semi-quicksand. People nearby became alerted to what was going on when they heard the children shouting, 'But what about Clip? Get Clip Daddy!'

'Clip's all right. Leave Clip. You keep walking.'

A man and his daughter came up to their dad.

'Need any help?' asked the man. Dad had crouched down on the sand and was encouraging the children to keep on walking back to him.

'They're on soft sand,' he whispered to the man, 'I don't know how soft it is. If they stop they might sink.'

'Good grief!' replied the man holding his daughter's hand tightly.

'Come on Mhari, don't stop. Hang on to Sean and bring him with you. Quickly if you can.'

Mhari and Sean walked steadily towards their dad, until at last they reached him and both clung on sobbing.

'What about Clip? Get Clip, Daddy,' wailed Sean.

'Is that your dog?' the man asked.

'Yes, but he's gone across the quicksand onto firmer stuff,' replied Dad.

'How can you tell?' asked the man.

'You can see by the way the sun reflects on the fine layer of water that lies on top of the quicksand. You get to recognise it if you live round here. We daren't let the dog come back this way.'

Clip was still harassing the seagull who was beginning to tire.

He tried lifting it in his mouth, but the gull pecked at him until he dropped it onto the sand again.

'Right,' said the man, 'my car's up on the path. If we drive to the other side of that stretch of quicksand, you'll be able to call your dog back that way.'

'Great!' said the children, and everyone ran to the car. There was no room on the path to turn the car around, so the man had to reverse quite a long way to make sure that Clip couldn't possibly run the wrong way.

For the first time, the man's daughter spoke.

'You love your dog, don't you?' She was talking to Mhari.

'Yes. We've had Clip since he was a puppy,' she replied.

'I've got a dog too, but he's not here today. I love my dog too.'

The man parked his car and opened the boot.

'I'm sure I had some here. Ah! There they are.' He had found a few dog biscuits in a brown bag and he handed them to Mhari's dad. They all moved onto the shoreline where the coarse grass gave way to a line of shingle, seaweed and drift-wood.

Clip had grown tired of teasing the gull. His mouth was full of feathers that had come away from it. He began looking for his family again.

'Here Clip! Come on Clip!' called Mhari.

'That's not loud enough,' said her dad, and he began bellowing. 'HERE CLIP! COME ON CLIP!'

The intelligent dog stood absolutely still. He hadn't expected his family to be so far away – and in the other direction. He stood as if trying to decide which way to go.

'Biscuits! Biscuits!' shouted Sean and his dad joined in, 'BISCUITS! BISCUITS!'

Clip couldn't resist. He bounded across the sand, and then romped around the children, snuffling in their pockets for the biscuits.

'Thanks,' said Dad to the man, 'Thanks a lot. I thought for a moment we were going to lose the dog. Thanks again.'

'It's OK,' said the man, 'It was lucky I brought the car down. This is a beautiful bit of coast, but I didn't realise it was so dangerous.'

'It's not so bad, once you get to know it. You learn to look for things like change of tide, or patches of quicksand.'

'Do you live round here then?' asked the man.

'Yes. That's our cottage over there – well actually you can only see the chimney from here.'

'Then you'll be our neighbour when we move in. We've bought Brough Head, the house at the top of the path.'

'Oh aye – the Big House. Pleased to meet you. Why don't you come back to our house for a cup of tea?' asked Mhari's dad.

'I'd love to,' said the man, 'Tell me what line of business are you in? Are you a fisherman?'

'No,' replied Mhari's dad, 'I'm a driver, heavy-goods mostly.'

'Well now, I've something to do with haulage myself . . . ' and the two men walked and talked their way back to the car.

'I like your dog,' said the girl quite shyly. 'Would you like to see my dog one day?'

Mhari said that she would, but all the time she was thinking, 'Surely these aren't the Snoots? They're far too nice!'